Levels
3-5

Level Up

HOMEWORK
BOOK

Author team: Greg and Lynn Byrd

LiveText

Heinemann is an imprint of Pearson Education Limited, a company incorporated in England and Wales, having its registered office at Edinburgh Gate, Harlow, Essex, CM20 2JE.
Registered company number: 872828

www.heinemann.co.uk

Heinemann is a registered trademark of Pearson Education Limited

Text © Pearson Education Limited 2008

First published 2008

12
10 9 8 7 6 5

British Library Cataloguing in Publication Data is available from the British Library on request.

ISBN 978 0 435537 38 8

Edited by Maggie Rumble
Designed by Pearson Education Ltd
Typeset by Tech-Set Ltd
Produced by Tech-Set Ltd
Original illustrations © Pearson Education Limited 2008
Illustrated by Beehive and Tech-Set Ltd
Cover design by Tom Cole (Seamonster Design)
Cover illustration by Max Ellis
Printed in China (CTPS / 05)

Acknowledgements

The author and publisher would like to thank the following individuals and organisations for permission to reproduce photographs:

Pearson Education Ltd / Tudor Photography p58; Shutterstock / Khoroshunova Olga p90

Every effort has been made to contact copyright holders of material reproduced in this book. Any omissions will be rectified in subsequent printings if notice is given to the publishers.

Contents

Welcome to Level Up Maths!

Level Up Maths is an inspirational new course for today's classroom. With stunning textbooks and amazing software, Key Stage 3 Maths has simply never looked this good!

The Homework Book has 18 units, with one homework page for each lesson in the Level Up 3–5 Textbook. The homework questions cover the same topics as the textbook pages, at the same levels.

This shows where to look for help on the LiveText CD.

Every homework starts with a question to practise your number skills.

The sub-levelled questions practise the topics covered in the lesson.

Your teacher may tell you to tick the questions to try.

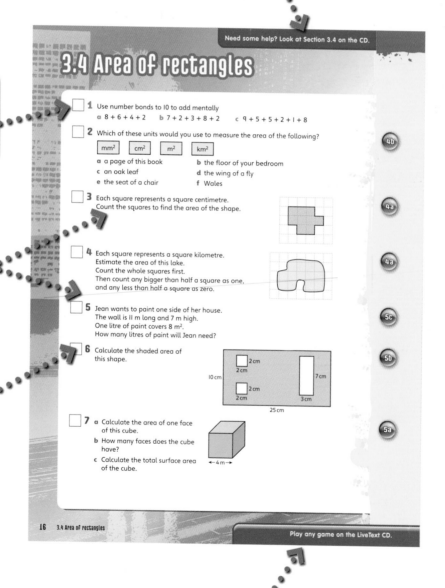

Need some help? Look at Section 3.4 on the CD.

3.4 Area of rectangles

1 Use number bonds to 10 to add mentally
  a 8 + 6 + 4 + 2   b 7 + 2 + 3 + 8 + 2   c 9 + 5 + 5 + 2 + 1 + 8

2 Which of these units would you use to measure the area of the following?

  mm²   cm²   m²   km²

  a a page of this book   b the floor of your bedroom
  c an oak leaf   d the wing of a fly
  e the seat of a chair   f Wales

3 Each square represents a square centimetre.
  Count the squares to find the area of the shape.

4 Each square represents a square kilometre.
  Estimate the area of this lake.
  Count the whole squares first.
  Then count any bigger than half a square as one,
  and any less than half a square as zero.

5 Jean wants to paint one side of her house.
  The wall is 11 m long and 7 m high.
  One litre of paint covers 8 m².
  How many litres of paint will Jean need?

6 Calculate the shaded area of this shape.

  2 cm
  2 cm
  10 cm
  2 cm
  2 cm
  7 cm
  3 cm
  25 cm

7 a Calculate the area of one face of this cube.
  b How many faces does the cube have?
  c Calculate the total surface area of the cube.
  ← 4 m →

4b
4a
4a
5c
5b
5a

16   3.4 Area of rectangles

Play any game on the LiveText CD.

This shows you the games to play on the LiveText CD. (Not for every homework.)

The LiveText CD

The LiveText CD in the back of this book has:

- The whole textbook on screen

> Explanations, to help you understand the Big Ideas.

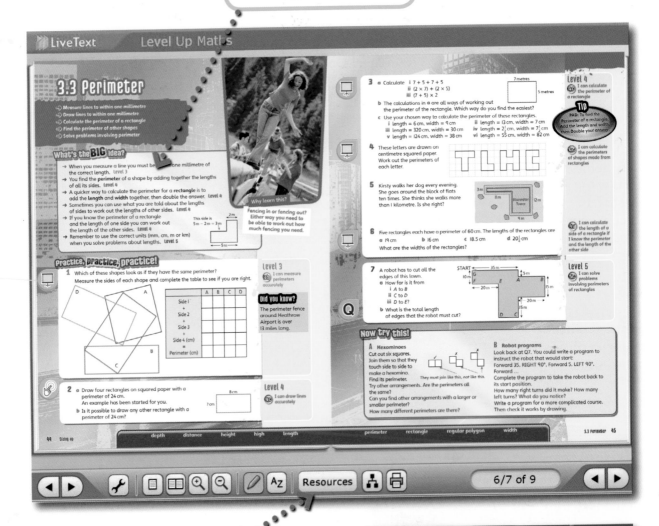

> Glossary to explain maths words. Play audio to hear translations in Bengali, Gujarati, Punjabi, Turkish and Urdu.

- Games to practise your maths skills.

1.1 Multiples, square and triangle numbers

1 Johan pays 48p for a pen. How much change does he get from £1? *52*

2

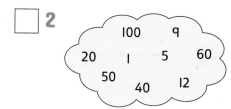

Write down the numbers from the cloud that are:
a multiples of 5
b multiples of 10
c multiples of both 5 and 10
d multiples of 4
e multiples of 4 and 10
f multiples of 3
g multiples of 3 and 4
h multiples of 2, 3, 4 and 10

3a

3 These patterns are made from squares.

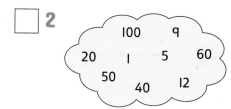

First pattern   Second pattern   Third pattern

Each pattern can be split into two square numbers.

1 × 1   2 × 2

1 + 4 = 5 squares

  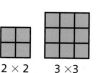
2 × 2   3 × 3

4 + 9 = 13 squares

4a

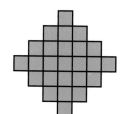 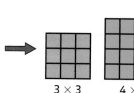
3 × 3   4 × 4

9 + 16 = 25 squares

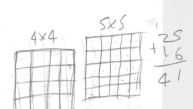
4×4   5×5   25 +16 41

a Draw the fourth pattern. Split it into two square numbers.
Find the total number of squares in the pattern. Use colours to help you. *41*

25 +36 61

b Explain how you could work out the total number of squares in the fifth pattern
without drawing it. How many squares are there in the fifth pattern? *you do the next squre nos. 61*
+36

c Work out how many squares there are in the sixth pattern. *42 78*

4 Using the pattern of squares above, work out how many squares there are
a in the tenth pattern *210*   b in the eleventh pattern. *100 110 24 224*

5c

1.2 Number patterns

1 Work out mentally:
   a 37 + 43   80   **b** 17 + 34   51   **c** 24 + 16 + 35   75

2 Copy these sequences and find the next three terms.
   a 1, 2, 3, 4, 5, 6, 7   **b** 2, 4, 6, 8, 10, 12, 14
   c 3, 5, 7, 9, 11, 14, 17   **d** 3, 8, 13, 18, 23, 28, 33
   e 3, 13, 23, 33, 43, 53, 63   **f** 3, 103, 203, 303, 403, 603, 503

3 Copy these sequences and find the next three terms.
   a 20, 19, 18, 17, 16, 15, 14   **b** 20, 18, 16, 14, 12, 10, 8
   c 20, 17, 14, 11, 8, 5, 2   **d** 200, 180, 160, 140, 130, 120, 110

4 All the numbers in this cloud are the missing numbers from these sequences.

   21   25   27   12   15   40

   a 6, 9, 12, 15, 18, 21, 24, 27, ...
   b 40, 35, 30, 25, 20, 15, 10, ...

   Copy the sequences and write the missing numbers in the correct boxes.

5 Copy these sequences and find the next three terms.
   a 0.1, 0.2, 0.3, 0.4, 0.5, 0.6, 0.7   **b** 0.5, 1.0, 1.5, 2.0, 2.5, 3.0, 3.5
   c 3.5, 3.4, 3.3, 3.2, 3.1, 3.0, 2.9   **d** 2.5, 2.2, 1.9, 1.6, 1.3, 1.1, 0.6

6 Match each description card with one of the sequence cards.

Starts at 16 and increases in steps of 4	16, 18, 20, 22, ...
Starts at 16 and decreases in steps of 4	16, 14, 12, 10, ...
Starts at 16 and decreases in steps of 2	16, 20, 24, 28, ...
Starts at 16 and increases in steps of 2	16, 12, 8, 4, ...

7 Describe these sequences. Give the first term and the term-to-term rule.
   a 5, 15, 25, 35, 45, ... +5   **b** 0, 7, 14, 21, 28, ... +7
   c 10.2, 10.6, 11.0, 11.4, 11.8, ... +6   **d** 6.8, 6.5, 6.2, 5.9, 5.6, ... +3

1.3 Terms of a sequence

1 a Copy and complete **i** 2 × 4 = 8   **ii** 3 × 4 = 12   **iii** 5 × 4 = 20
  b Add your answers from part **a** together. 40
  c Your answer to part **b** is a number in the four times table.
    Divide this answer by 4. What number do you get? 10

2 Copy these sequences. Work out the differences between the terms.
  Use the difference to work out the next two terms of each sequence.
    a 15, 10, 5, 0, −5, −10, −15   **b** 7, 5, 3, 1, −1, −3, −5
    c 27, 18, 9, 0, −9, −18, −27   **d** −2, −5, −8, −11, −14, −17

3 The dial on a freezer has six settings.
  These are the temperatures of the first
  three settings.
  These temperatures are the first three
  terms of a sequence.
  Work out the temperature of setting
  number 6. −24

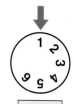 −12°C
 −14°C
 −16°C

4 Write down the next five terms of these sequences.

	Rule	First term	
a	Add 5	2	7, 12, 17, 22, 27
b	Subtract 4	16	12, 8, 4, 0, −4
c	Multiply by 2	4	8, 16, 32, 64, 128
d	Divide by 2	160	80, 40, 20, 10, 5

5 The first three terms in a sequence are 1, 2, 4, ...
  a What is the fourth number in the sequence? 6
  b Write down the term-to-term rule you used. +2
  c Write down two different ways to continue this number sequence.
      two times tables
          × 2

6 Write down the next five terms of these sequences.

	Term-to-term rule	First term	
a	+ 2	0	2, 4, 6, 8, 10
b	− 3	9	6, 3, 0, −3, −6
c	+ 4	− 50	−46, −42, −38, −34, −30
d	− 5	3	−2, −7, −12, −17, −22

7 The position-to-term rule of this sequence is 'multiply by 10 then subtract 5'.
  Copy and complete the table using this position-to-term rule.

Position	1	2	3	4	5
Term	5	15	25	35	45

1.4 Functions and mappings

1 Find the remainder when:

a 27 is divided by 4 3 b 28 is divided by 6 4 c 33 is divided by 5 3

2 ■ × ● = 24

Find as many pairs of numbers as you can for ■ and ●. 1×24 , 4 ×6
12×2 , 3×8

3 a Use the fact that 20 × 8 = 160 to complete the diagram.

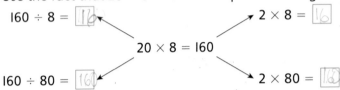

160 ÷ 8 = 16 2 × 8 = 16

20 × 8 = 160

160 ÷ 80 = 160 2 × 80 = 160

b Write down two more multiplications that could go with the diagram above.

4 Copy these function machines and find the missing outputs.

a
```
2 →            → 5
6 →   +3      → 9
100 →          → 103
```

b
```
3 →            → 12
4 →   ×4      → 16
100 →          → 400
```

c
```
20 →           → 15
10 →   −5      → 5
100 →          → 95
```

d
```
16 →           → 4
24 →   ÷4      → 6
100 →          → 25
```

5 These function machines have some input and output numbers missing.

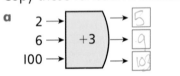

```
3 →                    → 4
8 →   ×3  →   −5      → 19
9 →                    → 22
```

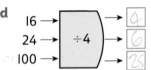

```
6 →                    → 9
10 →   ÷2  →   +6      → 11
2 →                    → 7
```

These are some number cards.

 2   4   6   9   10   19   22

Which of the number cards is **not** one of the missing numbers from the function machines?

6 Alun said:

> My function machine multiplies a number by 2 then subtracts 3 from the result.

a Which one of these mappings represents Alun's function machine?

    A $x \to 2(x - 3)$ **B** $x \to x - 3 \times 2$ **C** $x \to 2 \times x - 3$ **D** $x \to 2(x - 3)$

b Copy and complete this table using Alun's mapping.

x	1	2	3	4	5
y	-1	1	3	5	7

3b

3a

4a

5c

5a

1.5 Letters and unknowns

1 Write down the answers to:

a $\frac{1}{3} + \frac{1}{3} = \frac{1}{6}$ b $\frac{1}{5} + \frac{1}{5} = \frac{1}{10}$ c $\frac{1}{4} + \frac{1}{4} + \frac{1}{4} = \frac{1}{12}$ d $\frac{1}{2} + \frac{1}{2} + \frac{1}{2} = \frac{1}{6}$

2 Find the missing numbers in each of these.

a $10 + \boxed{4} = 14$ b $\boxed{12} + 6 = 18$ c $20 - \boxed{6} = 14$ d $\boxed{16} - 4 = 12$

3 Find the missing numbers in each of these.

a $3 \times \boxed{4} = 12$ b $\boxed{4} \times 5 = 20$ c $40 \div \boxed{5} = 8$ d $\boxed{} \div 4 = 10$

4 Write down the calculation you would do to solve these problems. Do *not* work out the answer.

a An apple farmer has 45 rows of trees. There are 15 trees in each row. How many trees are there altogether? 45×15

b Mike is putting a wooden roof on his treehouse. He uses 4 nails for each piece of wood. He has 160 nails. How many pieces of wood can he put on the roof? $160 \div 4$

c A bus has 27 people on board. When it stops at a bus stop, 15 people get off and 7 people get on. How many people are now on the bus? $(27 - 15) + 7$

5 Sasha has n songs on her MP3 player. Write expressions, using n, for the number of songs on her friends' MP3 players.

a Tao has 10 less songs than Sasha. $n - 10$

b Alice has 45 more songs than Sasha. $n + 45$

c Ursula has twice as many songs as Sasha. $n \times 2$

d Liam has three times as many songs as Sasha plus an extra 10 songs. $(n \times 3) + 10$

Sasha downloads another p songs from the internet to her MP3 player.

e How many songs does Sasha now have on her MP3 player? $n + p$

6 Match the pink description cards to the blue expression cards.

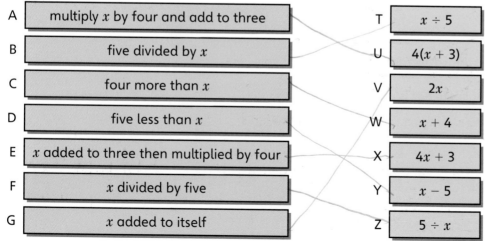

A multiply x by four and add to three	T $x \div 5$
B five divided by x	U $4(x + 3)$
C four more than x	V $2x$
D five less than x	W $x + 4$
E x added to three then multiplied by four	X $4x + 3$
F x divided by five	Y $x - 5$
G x added to itself	Z $5 \div x$

1.6 Patterns and sequences

1 For each of the following, subtract 5, then multiply by 3:
   a 15 *30*   **b** 23 *54*   **c** 35 *90*   **d** 47 *126*

A This number sequence is made from rhombuses.

First shape · Second shape · Third shape

3 rhombuses · 6 rhombuses · 9 rhombuses

2 Draw the next pattern in the sequence.   ③ⓑ

3 How many rhombuses are there in the fifth pattern? *15*   ③ⓑ

4 Copy and complete the table.   ④ⓑ

Pattern number	1	2	3	4	5
Number of rhombuses	3	6	9	12	15

5 Describe the term-to-term rule. *+3*   ④ⓑ

6 Write down the position-to-term rule in words. *3 times table*   ⑤ⓒ

7 a Use your rule to predict how many rhombuses there are in the sixth pattern. *18*   ⑤ⓑ
   b Test whether your rule works by drawing the sixth pattern.

B This number sequence is made from counters.

First · Second · Third

3 counters · 5 counters · 7 counters

Repeat questions 2 to 7 for this sequence of counters.

Q3–11 counters Q5–+2 Q6–all odd no's 9 counters

Q4: | Pattern no | 1 | 2 | 3 | 4 | 5 |
| No of counters | 3 | 5 | 7 | 9 | 11 |

C This number sequence is made from squares.

First · Second · Third

1 square · 5 squares · 9 squares

Repeat questions 2 to 7 for this sequence of squares.

Q3–17 Q4: | Pattern no | 1 | 2 | 3 | 4 | 5 |
| no of squares | 1 | 5 | 9 | 13 | 17 |
Q5–+4

Play any game on the LiveText CD

2.1 Place value

1 In this number wheel, opposite numbers add up to 20.
Write down the numbers that are in positions A to F.

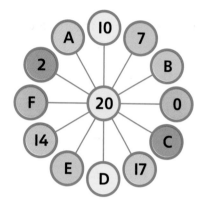

A = 3   e = 13
B = 19   f = 20
c = 18
d = 10

2 Write these numbers in figures.

a seventy six   76   b seven hundred and six   706

c seven thousand six hundred 7600 d seven thousand and sixty 7060

e seven thousand and six 7006   f seven thousand seven hundred and sixty 7760

 3a

3 Write these numbers in words.

a 67   b 607   c 6700   d 6070

sixty seven | six hundred and seven | six thousand seven hundred | six thousand and seventy

3a

4 Write down the value of the 9 in each of these numbers.

a 7926   b 28349   c 12.91   d 61.39

hundred   unit   tenths   hundredths

3a

5 Kim has these cards:

| 2 | 4 | • | 1 |

Kim says that the smallest number she can make is 24.1
Kim is wrong. Write down the smallest number that Kim can make.   1.24

4b

6 Work out

a 43 × 10 430   b 43 ÷ 10 4.3   c 43 × 100 4300

d 275 ÷ 10 27.5   e 275 × 1000 275 000   f 275 ÷ 100 2.75

4a

7 Work out

a 0.75 × 100 75   b 7.5 × 1000 7500

c 75.2 ÷ 100 0.752   d 75.2 ÷ 1000 0.0752

5c

8 1 tonne = 1000 kg   1 kg = 1000g   1 g = 1000 mg

Work out

a 1.3 tonnes = ...1300..... kg   b 35 g = ...35000..... mg

c 0.375 kg = ...375..... g   d 42 kg = ...0.042..... tonnes

5c

2.2 Addition and subtraction

1 ★ × O = 18 1×18 , 2×9 , 3×6
Find as many pairs of numbers as you can for ★ and O.

3b

2 Mentally add all these pairs of numbers. Show your method in writing.

a 21 + 39 60   b 55 + 25 80   c 86 + 34 120
d 18 + 60 78   e 40 + 68 108   f 88 + 87 175

working out for Q3
68 –   82
25   45 –
43   37

3 Do these subtractions. Show your method in writing.

a 68 − 25 43   b 82 − 45 37   c 70 − 16 54

3a

4 On each side of the shape, the numbers in the two circles add together to give
the number in the square between them.
Copy and complete these.

3b

a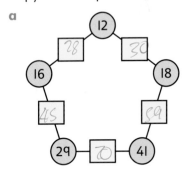

b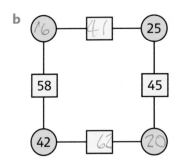

5 Copy and complete these calculations using complements to 100.

a 66 + 34 = 100   b 19 + 81 = 100   c 45 + 55 = 100

4c

6 Work out

a   1 6 . 3
   + 3 1 . 6
   ───────
     47.9

b   4 7 . 4 0
   + 1 8 . 3 5
   ─────────
     65.75

c   4 3 . 4
   − 0 2 . 6
   ───────
     40.8

d   6 1 2 . 3 5
   − 2 3 1 . 5 1
   ───────────
     380.84

4b

7 Copy and complete this money pyramid.
Find each missing amount by adding the two bricks below it.

£1.30 + £2.05
£1.25 + £1.30

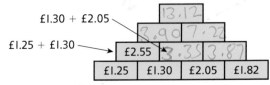

4b

2.3 Positive and negative numbers

1 The first four multiples of 5 are 5, 10, 15, 20.
Copy and complete
  a The first four multiples of 2 are 2, 4, 6, 8
  b The first four multiples of 4 are 4, 8, 12, 16
  c The first four multiples of 10 are 10, 20, 30, 40

Use this weather map to answer questions 2, 3 and 4

2 Calculate the new temperature in
  a Birmingham, after the temperature rises by 4°C   3°C
  b Newcastle, after it warms up by 3°C.   −1°C

3b

3 Calculate the new temperature in
  a Exeter, after the temperature falls by 4°C   −3°C
  b London, after it cools down by 9°C   −5°C
  c Swansea, after the temperature falls by 10°C.   −6°C

3a

4 Write the temperatures shown on the weather
map in order, coldest first.
  −4°C, −1°C, 0°C, 1°C, 2°C, 4°C, 4°C

4b

5 Write these temperature changes as number sentences.
Calculate the end temperature.
  a − 8°C rises by 7°C   −1°C   **b** 5°C falls by 7°C   −2°C   **c** − 7°C falls by 2°C   −9°C

4a

Stirling
−2°C•

Newcastle
−4°C•

Belfast
0°C •

Birmingham
• −1°C

Swansea
• 4°C   London
         4°C •
Exeter
• 1°C

6 In this number wheel, opposite numbers
add up to −5.
Write down the numbers that are in
positions L, M, N, P and Q.
  L = −15   M = −1   N = +2
  P = −5   Q = −9

5a

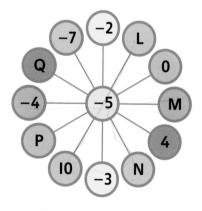

−7   −2   L
Q   0
−4   −5   M
P   4
10   −3   N

7 Work out
  a −5 − 2 = +3   **b** 5 − −2 = 7   **c** −5 − −2 = −3   **d** −5 + −6 = −11

5a

2.4 Decimals

1 $1^2 = 1 \times 1 = 1$
$2^2 = 2 \times 2 = 4$
$3^2 = 3 \times 3 = 9$
Continue this pattern up to $15^2 = 15 \times 15 = 225$.

2 The table shows the body temperature of some animals.

Animal	Temperature (°F)	
Human	98.6	4
Rat	100.4	7
Dog	100.9	8
Mouse	97.7	3
Alligator	75.2	1
Horse	100.2	6
Gorilla	96.4	2
Donkey	99.4	5

Numbered from coldest

a Which animal has the warmest body temperature? *Dog*

b Which animal has the coldest body temperature? *Alligator.*

c Arrange the temperatures in order, starting with the coldest.

3 Copy the pairs of numbers below.
Write the correct sign, > or <, between each pair of numbers.

a 97.74 ☐< 100   **b** £0.25 ☐> 5p   **c** −0.1 ☐< −5.0

4 Raul has tried to put these decimal numbers in order, starting with the smallest.

8.2, 8.07, 8.35, 8.77, 9.0

a Which numbers has Raul put in the wrong place? *8.07*

b Rewrite the numbers in the correct order. *8.07, 8.2, 8.35, 8.77, 9.0*

5 Put these cards in order, starting with the smallest.

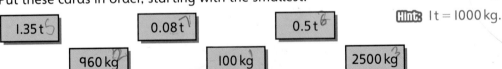

| 1.35 t | 5 | | | 0.08 t | 7 | | | 0.5 t | 6 | **Hint:** 1 t = 1000 kg. |

| 960 kg | 4 | | 100 kg | 1 | | 2500 kg | 3 |

6 Put these cards in order, starting with the smallest.
100 cm = 1 m
1 cm = 10 mm

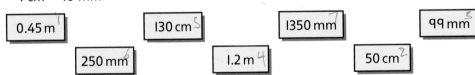

| 0.45 m | 1 | | 130 cm | 5 | | 1350 mm | 7 | | 99 mm | 3 |

| 250 mm | 6 | | 1.2 m | 4 | | 50 cm | 2 |

2.5 Square numbers and multiplication

1 Calculate the new temperature in
a Glasgow, after the temperature rises by 5°C—1?
b York, after it warms up by 3°C 2°C
c Pembroke, after the temperature falls by 10°C —2°C
d Manchester, after it cools down by 9°C. —3°C

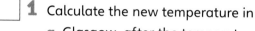

Glasgow −4°C

York −1°C

Pembroke 8°C

Manchester 6°C

2 Copy this multiplication grid.
Complete the grid as quickly as you can.
Use a stopwatch to time how long it takes you.

×	2	5	3	8	10	4	9	7
4	8	20	12	32	40	16	36	28
6	12	30	18	48	60	24	54	42
10	20	50	30	80	100	40	90	70
7	14	35	21	56	70	28	63	42
3	6	15	9	24	30	12	27	21
5	10	25	15	40	50	20	45	35
2	4	10	6	16	20	8	18	14
9	18	45	27	72	90	36	81	63

4b

3 The numbers in the circles are multiplied to give the numbers in the squares between them.
Use multiplication and division facts to work out the missing values.

4a

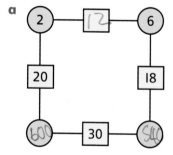

a

2 — 12 — 6

20 ... 18

600 — 30 — 540

b

200

40 ... 50

240

32

4 — 8

4 Work out
a 11 × 11 121   b 12 to the power 2   c 13² 169   d 14 squared 196

5c

5 Choose the correct answer **A** or **B**, for each of these.
a 3.2 × 20   A 6.4   B (64)
b 5.4 × 40   A 2160   B (216)
c 1.56 × 50   A (78)   B 780

5c

2.6 Using a calculator

1 Samir shares out his 459 conkers equally between his three best friends.
How many conkers do each of his friends get? *153*

2 Joanna uses her calculator to work out 28.3 + 41.9
The display shows 702. This answer is wrong.
   a Use your calculator to find the correct answer. *70.2*
   b What do you think Joanna did wrong? *She didn't put a decimal*

3c

3 These are some of the keys on a calculator.

7	8	9	DEL	AC
4	5	6	×	÷
1	2	3	+	−
0	·	+/−	ANS	=

Copy and complete the keys you need to press to work out these questions.
Make sure you write the keys in the correct order.

   a 27.5 + 306   2 7 · 5 + 3 0 6 =
   b 80.5 × 6.2   8 0 · 5 × 6 · 2 =

3c

4 Use your calculator to work out:
   a −12 − 3 *−15*   **b** 21 + −4 *17*   **c** −3 + −20 *−23*   **d** 10 − −12 *= 22*

3b

5 Estimate the answers to these:
   a 496 + 308 *= 800*   **b** 721 − 189   **c** 2981 − 209
   d 3906 + 97 *= 3900*   **e** 21 × 39   **f** 11.3 × 5.3

4b

6 Use your calculator to work out £7.75 + £4.75 *£12.50*

4b

7 Craig bought a computer game for £32.75 and a magazine for £2.85
   a Use your calculator to work out the total cost. *£35.60*
   b Craig paid with four £10 notes.
      How much change did he receive? *£4.40*

4a

8 Bird food costs £1.39 per packet.
Bryn has £10 to spend on bird food.
   a How many packets of bird food can he buy? *7*
   b What is the total cost? *£9.73*
   c How much change would he have? *27p*

4a

3.1 Mission to Mars

1 Find the missing numbers in each of these.

a 12 + [8] = 20   b [14] − 7 = 11   c 4 × [6] = 24   d [21] ÷ 7 = 3

e [12] + 4 = 16   f [13] − 8 = 5   g [7] × 5 = 35   h 9 ÷ [3] = 3

2 Which of these nets are correct for a **closed** cube like this one?

a 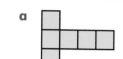   b   c 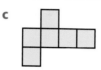   d

e 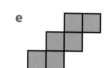   f   g 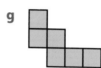   h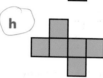

3 This table shows the number of faces, edges and vertices of the solid shapes below. Copy and complete the table. Shape A has been done for you.

A   B   C  D   E   F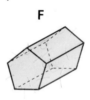

Shape	A	B	C	D	E	F
Faces	4	4	6	4	6	7
Edges	6	8	10	8	12	14
Vertices	4	5	6	6	8	10

4 Match each shape with the correct net for the shape.

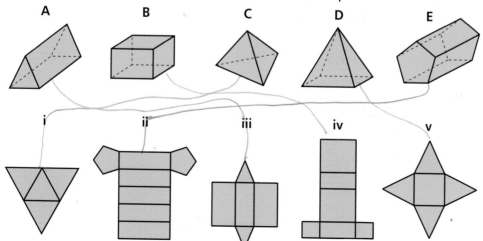

3.2 Measurement

1 Use your calculator to work out the answers to these questions.

 a 12.3 + 45.9 56.2 b 71.4 − 28.3 43.1 c 4.2 × 3.6 d 112.5 ÷ 9 12.5

2 How much does one division represent on each of these scales?
Write down the number the arrows are pointing to.

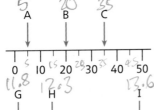

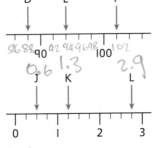

a A 5 B 20 C 35

b D 88 E 94 F 102

G 11.8 H 12.3 I 13.6

c

d J 0.6 K 1.3 L 2.9

3   cm   km   cm²   km²   m   mm²   mm   m²

Choose a suitable unit for measuring each of the following.

 a The distance Carlos cycled in one hour km²

 b The height of a kitchen worktop. mc

 c The area of a TV screen. m²

 d The width of your sitting room. cm²

 e The area of the wall you are facing. mm²

 f The length of an ant. mm

4 Choose the answer you think is closest to the real value for each of these statements.

 a The area of a calculator screen is … 10.03 mm² / 10.03 cm² / 10.03 m²

 b The area of a 10p coin is … 5 m² / 5 cm² / 5 mm²

 c The area of the roof of a house is … 104 mm² / 104 m² / 104 cm²

5 Convert these measurements so that they are all in millimetres.

 a 2.7 cm 270mm b 2.7 m 2700mm c 0.2 cm 20mm d 0.27 cm 270mm

6 Convert these measurements so that they are all in metres.

 a 270 cm 2.7m b 27 cm 0.27m c 2 cm 0.2m d 2700 mm 0.27m

7 Put these measurements in order of size, from the smallest to the largest.

 a 36 mm   d 2.7 cm   c 500 mm   b 0.35 m

8 A bicycle travels 2.5 m each time a wheel completes one revolution.
Lars cycles 3 km to work

 a How many revolutions does his bicycle wheel complete in 3 km? 12 revolution

Lars works from Monday to Friday each week.

 b How many revolutions does his bicycle wheel make in one week
   of cycling to work and back? 60 revolutions

3.3 Perimeter

1 Write these numbers in figures.

a forty nine *49*

b four hundred and nine *409*

c four thousand nine hundred *4900*

d four thousand and ninety *4090*

e four thousand and nine *4009*

f four hundred and ninety *490*

2 a The shape below is made from two triangles.
Measure the sides of each triangle and complete the table.

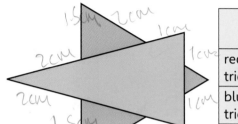

1.5cm 2cm 1cm 2cm 1cm 1cm 2cm 1.5cm 2cm

	Side 1 + (cm)	Side 2 + (cm)	Side 3 (cm)	= perimeter (cm)
red triangle	*4 cm*	*4 cm*	*4 cm*	*12 cm*
blue triangle	*5 cm*	*5 cm*	*2.5 cm*	*12.5 cm*

 3b

b Add the perimeter of the red triangle to the perimeter of the blue triangle. *24.5*

c Is this answer the same as the perimeter of the whole shape? *NO*

3 Measure each side of this trapezium. *7.5cm 1cm*
Work out the perimeter of the trapezium.

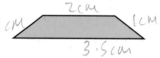
2cm 1cm 3.5cm

3b

4 Draw two different size rectangles with a perimeter of 20 cm.

4c

5 Calculate the perimeter of a rectangular swimming pool of length 25 m
and width 13 m. *25 38 +13 × 2 38 76   76cm*

4c

6 Gavin measures some of the lengths of the walls in
his bedroom.
This is the diagram he draws.
Calculate the perimeter of Gavin's bedroom.

13m

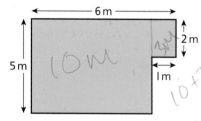
6 m
2 m
5 m *10m*
1 m
10+3=13m

4b

7 Four rectangles each have a perimeter of 40 cm. The widths of the rectangles are

a (5 cm)   b 9 cm   c 12.5 cm   d 19.5 cm

What are the lengths of the rectangles?

15 cm

4a

8 Chloe wants to put a fence around her lawn.
This diagram shows some of the
measurements of her lawn.

a Copy the diagram and write on all the missing
measurements.

b Work out the total length of fencing that
Chloe needs to go around the whole lawn. *96m*

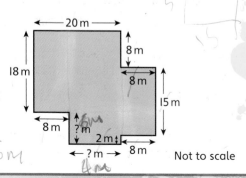
20 m
8 m
18 m
8 m
15 m
8 m *6m* ?m
2 m
? m 8 m
Not to scale

5c

3.4 Area of rectangles

1 Use number bonds to 10 to add mentally

a $8 + 6 + 4 + 2$ *20* b $7 + 2 + 3 + 8 + 2$ *22* c $9 + 5 + 5 + 2 + 1 + 8$ *30*

2 Which of these units would you use to measure the area of the following?

| mm² | cm² | m² | km² |

a a page of this book *cm²*   b the floor of your bedroom *m²*

c an oak leaf *mm²*   d the wing of a fly *mm*

e the seat of a chair *cm²*   f Wales *km²*

3 Each square represents a square centimetre.
Count the squares to find the area of the shape. *9²*

4 Each square represents a square kilometre.
Estimate the area of this lake.
Count the whole squares first.
Then count any bigger than half a square as one,
and any less than half a square as zero. *14²*

5 Jean wants to paint one side of her house.
The wall is 11 m long and 7 m high.
One litre of paint covers 8 m².
How many litres of paint will Jean need? *3*

6 Calculate the shaded area of
this shape. *221 cm²*

```
  7 80
-   29
  221
```

Diagram: rectangle 25 cm wide, 10 cm high, with squares labelled 4, 2 cm by 2 cm, and a vertical white rectangle 7 cm by 3 cm.

7 a Calculate the area of one face
of this cube. *16 m²*

b How many faces does the cube
have? *6*

c Calculate the total surface area
of the cube. *96 m²*

←4 m→

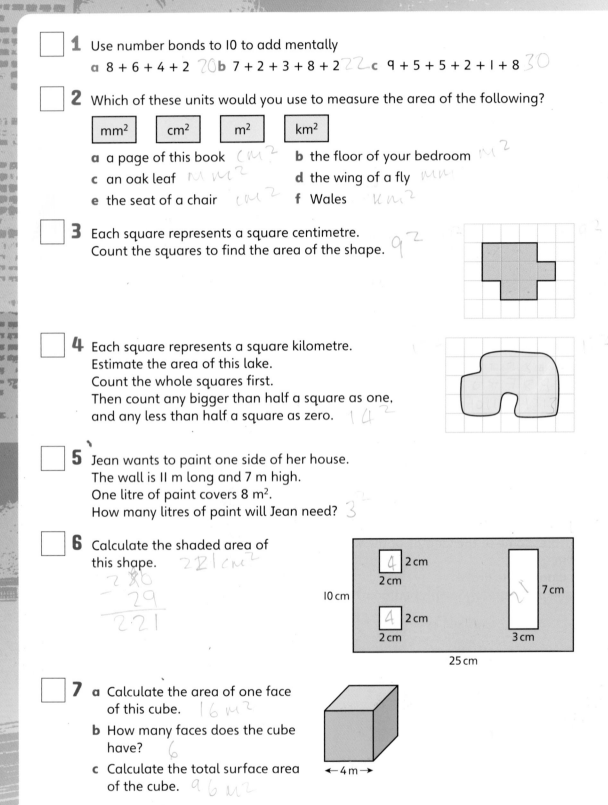

4.1 Fractions

1 Use your calculator to work out
a $15 + -4 = 11$ b $-15 - 4 = -19$ c $-15 + -4 = -19$ d $15 - -4 = 19$

2 Write down which of the diagrams have the equivalent fraction shaded.

A   B   C   D   E

a, b, c, d and e have equivilent fraction shaded.

3 Copy each diagram below.
Shade each one so that the fraction shaded is equivalent to:

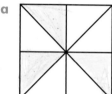 a

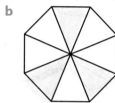 b

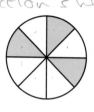

c

4 Copy each diagram and shade the fraction shown.

 a   b   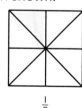 c   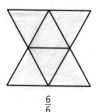 d

$\frac{5}{6}$ $\frac{3}{10}$ $\frac{1}{8}$ $\frac{6}{6}$

5 Change each improper fraction to a mixed number.
a $\frac{12}{5}$ *2/5*   b $\frac{11}{7}$ *4/7*   c $\frac{10}{3}$ *3 1/3*   d $\frac{9}{8}$ *1 1/8*

6 Work out each of the following.
If necessary, write your answer as a mixed number.
a $\frac{3}{8} + \frac{3}{8}$ *6/8*   b $\frac{5}{8} - \frac{3}{8}$ *2/8*   c $\frac{9}{10} + \frac{4}{10}$ *13/10*   d $\frac{10}{17} - \frac{3}{17}$ *7/17*
e $\frac{12}{19} + \frac{7}{19}$ *19/19*   f $\frac{12}{19} - \frac{7}{19}$ *5/19*   g $\frac{1}{5} + \frac{2}{5} + \frac{3}{5} + \frac{4}{5} + \frac{3}{5} + \frac{2}{5} + \frac{1}{5}$ *16/5*

7 Abraham had some marbles. He gave $\frac{1}{8}$ to Jo, $\frac{1}{8}$ to Jill and $\frac{3}{8}$ to Jackie.
What fraction did Abraham have left?

1/8 left for himself.

4.2 Equivalent fractions and simplifying

1 Sammi has these cards.

| 0 | I | 2 | 3 | • |

  a What is the largest number he can make using these cards? *3 21.0*
  b What is the smallest number he can make using these cards? *0.123*

2 Match each red card with its equivalent fraction blue card.
   Which two cards have no equivalent fraction?

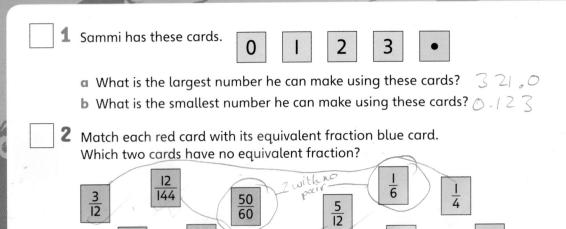

$\frac{3}{12}$ $\frac{12}{144}$ $\frac{50}{60}$ *2 with no pair* $\frac{1}{6}$ $\frac{1}{4}$

$\frac{80}{100}$ $\frac{25}{60}$ $\frac{5}{12}$ $\frac{1}{12}$ $\frac{4}{5}$

3 Copy and complete these equivalent fractions.

  a $\frac{1}{8} = \frac{3}{\boxed{24}}$ **b** $\frac{3}{7} = \frac{\boxed{15}}{35}$ **c** $\frac{\boxed{3}}{5} = \frac{15}{25}$ **d** $\frac{15}{\boxed{20}} = \frac{45}{60}$

4 Use the numbers on these cards.
   Write down four fractions that are equivalent to $\frac{3}{8}$. One has been done for you. $\frac{30}{80}$

| 30 | 6 | 15 | 9 | 800 | 80 | 16 | 300 | 24 | 40 |

   3/80   *6/16*   *300/800*   *9/28*   *15/40*

5 Draw two copies of the grid.
   Shade in $\frac{2}{5}$ of one, and $\frac{1}{3}$ of the other.
   Use your diagrams to show which is the bigger
   fraction $\frac{2}{5}$ or $\frac{1}{3}$.   *2/5*

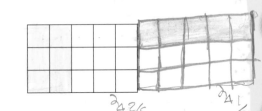

2/5   *1/3*

6 Put these fractions into their lowest terms
  a $\frac{5}{20}$ *1/4*   **b** $\frac{8}{10}$ *4/5*   **c** $\frac{25}{70}$ *5/14*   **d** $\frac{6}{42}$ *1/7*   **e** $\frac{72}{108} = \frac{36}{54} \to \frac{18}{27} \div 9 = \frac{2}{3}$

7 Convert these terminating decimals into fractions.
   Give the fractions in their lowest terms.
  a 0.8 $\frac{8}{10} \div 2 = \frac{4}{5}$ **b** 0.08 $\frac{2}{8} \cdot 25$ **c** 0.008 $\frac{0.8}{1000} = \frac{4}{50}$ **d** 0.17 $\frac{17}{100}$ **e** 0.125 $\frac{125}{100} = \frac{25}{200}$

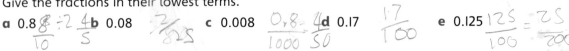

$\div 5 \quad \frac{5}{40} \div 5 = \frac{1}{8} =$

$\frac{2}{250}$

4.3 Fractions of amounts

1 Anya has £23.35.
She spends £16.49
How much does she have left? £6.86

2 a Finding one sixth of an amount is the same as dividing by 6 .
b $\frac{50}{7}$ is another way of writing 50 ⊟ 7.

3 What is
a half of 110? 55
b one sixth of 42? 7
c one tenth of 560? 56
d a quarter of 96? 24

4 Work out the answers to the following.
a $\frac{1}{2}$ of £60 £30
b $\frac{1}{3}$ of £60 £20
c $\frac{1}{4}$ of £60 £15
d $\frac{1}{5}$ of £60 £12

5 Find
a $\frac{2}{3}$ of £24 £16
b $\frac{3}{4}$ of £24 £18
c $\frac{5}{6}$ of £24 £20
d $\frac{7}{8}$ of £24 £21

6 Two thirds of a person's bodyweight is water.
Ajay weighs 57kg.
How much of his body weight is water?
$\frac{2}{3}$ of £24 = 38kg

7 One hundred £1 coins weigh 950 g.
$\frac{7}{10}$ of each coin is copper.
What is the weight of the copper
in the one hundred £1 coins?
$\frac{7}{10}$ of 950g = 665g

8 Each of the following items are in a sale.
Work out   i how much you would save
            ii the new cost.
a Ice skates – were £72, now a third off! £24, £48, £124
b Ski jacket – was £60, now one fifth off! £12, £48, £12
c Snowboard – was £180, save one quarter! £45, £135, £45

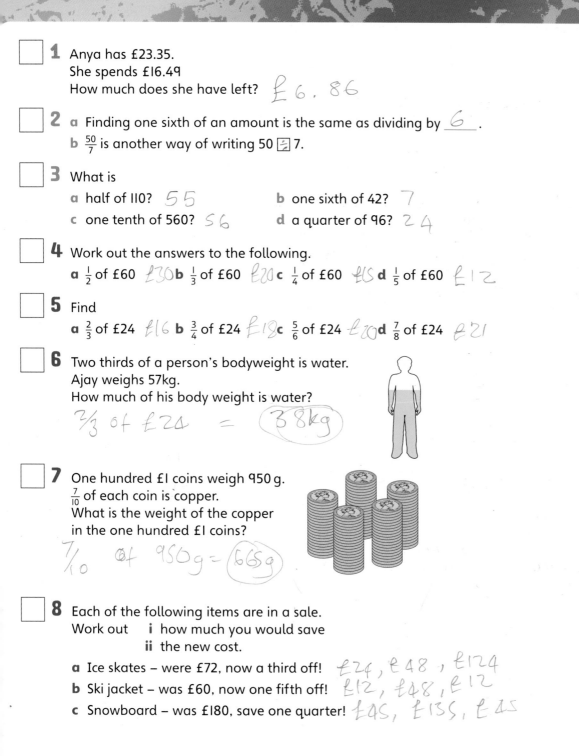

4.4 Percentages

1 Calculate the new temperature when a temperature of:
  a −5°C rises by 3°C − 2°C   **b** 6°C falls by 9°C − 3°C
  c −3°C goes up 8°C   5 °C   **d** −2°C drops by 3°C − 5°C

2 What percentage of each shape is shaded?

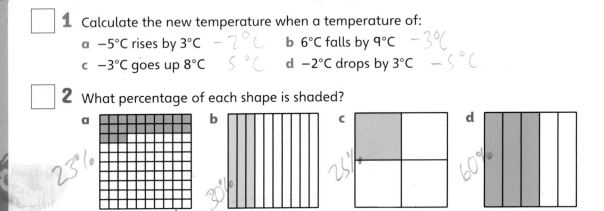

  a 23%   **b** 30%   **c** 25%   **d** 60%

3 What fraction of the shapes in Q2 are unshaded?
  (a) 77%   (b) 70%   (c) 75%   (d) 40%

4 85% of Alan's garden is lawn.
  What percentage of Alan's garden is not lawn?   15%

5 Write each percentage as a fraction in its lowest terms.
  a 20% 5/25 **b** 25% 1/4 **c** 36% 21/25 **d** 60% 6/10 **e** 85% 17/50
  20/100 = 10/50 = 5/25 25/100 = 5/20 = 1/4 36/100 = 42/50 = 21/25 60/100 = 6/10 85/100 = 17/50

6 Write the values **a** to **j** to complete the table.

Decimal	Fraction	Percentage
a 0.35	$\frac{35}{100}$	35%
0.7	**b** $\frac{70}{100}$	70%
c 0.40	$\frac{2}{5}$	40% **d**
0.07	**e** $\frac{7}{100}$	7% **f**
g 0.42	$\frac{21}{50}$	42% **h**
i 0.04	**j** $\frac{4}{100}$	4%

7 Group the cards into equivalent fractions, decimals and percentages.
  Which three cards do not belong to any group?

  $\frac{11}{25}$ 15% $\frac{4}{25}$ 0.16   44% $\frac{3}{20}$ 0.15
  16%   0.44   38% $\frac{38}{50}$ 0.83

4.5 Finding a percentage of an amount

1 Estimate the answers to these.
  a 388 − 106 *500*
  b 2890 + 1018 *3900*
  c 7212 − 2894 *4300*
  d 19.6 × 4.2 *76*

2 Find 10% of
  a 70
  b 30 m
  c £200
  d 170 ml

3 At one time the heaviest man in the world weighed 480 kg.
He lost 10% of his weight in less than two months.
Work out 10% of 480 kg to see how much weight he lost.

4 10% of the weight of a breakfast cereal is protein.
How much protein is there in a 30 g serving of this breakfast cereal?

5 Tom is a football agent.
He earns 10% of a player's transfer fee.
How much does Tom earn when a player's transfer fee is £12 000 000?

6 Work out the following:
  a 20% of £120
  b 40% of £60
  c 80% of £30

7 80% of the weight of a sugar-coated breakfast cereal is carbohydrate.
How much carbohydrate is there in a 30 g serving of this cereal?

8 Work out:
  a 25% of 160
  b 50% of 700 g
  c 75% of 4000 litres

9 By working out 10% and then 5%, find 15% of
  a £500
  b £2400
  c £3

Hint: You can change £3 into pence.

10 Jim pays £20 per hour for piano lessons.
Next month the price will increase by 15%.
What will the lessons cost next month?

4.6 Mental calculation

1 The numbers in the two circles add together to give the number in the square between them.
Copy and complete.

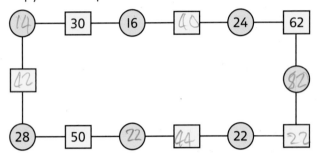

2 Henry VIII was king of England from 1509 to 1547.
Use counting up to work out how long he was king. *38 years*

3 Find the difference by counting up from the smaller number to the larger number.
   a 475 − 398 *77*   **b** 793 − 755 *38*   **c** 974 − 928

4 Find the difference by counting up from the smaller number to the larger number.
   a 3000 − 1556 *1444* **b** 5010 − 2510 *2500* **c** 6066 − 2442 *1468*

5 Add these near doubles.
   a 6.5 + 6.8 *13.3* **b** 8.4 + 8.7 *17.1*   **c** 12.6 + 12.7 *25.3*

6 Use doubling and halving to work out:
   a 44 × 50 *2200* **b** 21 × 50 *1050*   **c** 86 × 5 *430*   **d** 20 × 2.7 *54*

7 When full, a storage tank contains 1200 litres of oil.
How much oil is in it when it is
   a 50% full? *600* **b** 25% full? *300*   **c** 10% full?
   d 5% full?   **e** $2\frac{1}{2}$% full?   **Hint** Use your answer to 5% to help

8 **a** What is 50% of 74 kg? *37 kg*
   b What is 20% of £35?
   c Jenny gets paid £12 per hour. Her wages go up by 15%.
      What is her new hourly rate?
   d A child is given 75% of an adult dose of medicine.
      The adult dose is 20 millilitres. What is the child's dose?

3c

3b

3a

4b

4b

4a

4a

5.1 Averages

☐ **1** Copy and complete

    a   2 3 . 4
        + 3 5 . 2
        58 . 6

    b   7 6 . 5
        + 1 5 . 7
        92 . 2

    c   9 8 . 4
        − 4 5 . 2
        53 . 2

    d   4 8 . 3
        − 1 5 . 6
        32 . 7

☐ **2** Sam works in a cafe. She sells different types of drinks.
One morning she sells 17 mugs of coffee, 25 mugs of tea, 22 mugs of hot chocolate and 13 mugs of soup.
Which was the most common drink that Sam sold? *hot chocolate*

☐ **3** Connor carried out a survey on his class. He asked them to name their favourite sport.
4 liked football, 8 rugby, 13 athletics, 4 basketball and 3 tennis.
Which sport was liked the most? *athletics*

☐ **4** A riding stables had the following number of people on their beach rides one week.

    32   35   32   34   38   40   37

    a Work out the range of the number of people. *8*

    b Work out the mode of the number of people. *32*

    On one of the days, the ages of the riders were recorded.
These are the results.

Age of riders	5–14	15–24	25–34	35–44	45–54	55–64
Frequency	4	10	8	12	1	5

    c What is the modal group? *15–24*

☐ **5** Lynn has five dogs. Their ages are:
    4   12   8   11   8
Work out
    a the mean *8.6*   **b** the median *8*   **c** the mode *8*   **d** the range. *8*

☐ **6** Isleta keeps chickens.
She records the number of eggs that they lay each day for 15 days.
Here are her results.
Work out

Number of eggs	Frequency
1	2
2	6
3	2
4	3
5	2

    a the mean *3*
    b the mode *2*
    c the median. *2*

☐ **7** Greg has these number cards. He can't read the number on one of the cards.

    The mean of the numbers on the cards is 6.
What is the number on the card that Greg can't read? *5*

5.2 Extracting data

1 Work out

a 26 × 10 *260*   b 68 ÷ 10 *6.8*   c 81 × 100 *8100*

d 324 ÷ 10 *32.4* e 29 × 1000 *29000* f 560 ÷ 100 *5.6*

2 Catrin asked her friends what flavour ice cream they liked best.
She drew a bar chart of her results.

a What is the favourite flavour ice cream of Catrin's friends? *Strawberry*

b How many people said they liked vanilla best? *4*

c How many friends took part in Catrin's survey? *18*

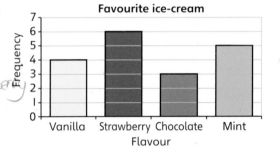

Favourite ice-cream

3 Santo drives a delivery van.
This bar chart shows the number of deliveries he makes each day.

a What is the modal group? *11-15*

b How many days does this bar chart show? *25*

c Which delivery group did Santo make twice? *1-5*

Santo's deliveries

4 John takes people horse riding on the beach.
The dual bar chart shows the height of low tide and high tide during one week in July.

a What is the height of the low tide on Monday? *1.2*

b What is the difference in height between the low tide on Sunday and the low tide on Monday? *0.2*

c What is the height of the high tide on Saturday? *5.9*

d Which day has the biggest difference in height between high tide and low tide? *Wednesday*

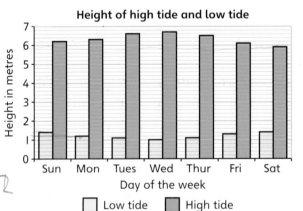

Height of high tide and low tide

3a

4b

5b

5.3 Interpreting graphs

1 The following cards show some temperatures.

| −1°C | 3°C | −5°C | 0°C | 6°C | −2°C | 8°C | −7°C |

Draw a number line from −10°C to +10°C. Place the cards in the correct position.

−7°C −5°C −2°C −1°C, 0°C, 3°C, 6°C, 8°C

2 Yvonne sells hot pies.
The graph shows the number of pies she sold in one year.

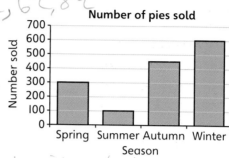

Number of pies sold

a How many pies did Yvonne sell in the autumn? 450

b In which season did Yvonne sell 100 pies? Summer

c What can you say about the number of pies Yvonne sold? The hotter it got less pies were sold.

3b

3 Craig joins a slimming club.
He is weighed at the start of every month.
This graph shows his weight loss over 1 year.

Weight

a Between which months was Craig's weight 100 kg? May

b How much did Craig weigh at the start of March? 112

c What is the difference in Craig's weight at the start of January and at the start of December? 40 kg

d What can you say about Craig's weight loss? he lost wieght by the end of the day

4b

4 This pie chart shows the favourite holiday destination of some people.

Favourite holiday destinations

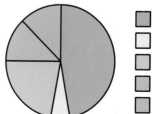

Spain
Portugal
France
Italy
Greece

a Which holiday destination was chosen by most people? Spain

b Which two holiday destinations were equally popular? Italy and greece.

5c

5.4 Probability in words

1 Copy and complete this multiplication grid.

×	2	5	8	3	9
3	6	15	24	9	27
6	12	30	48	18	54
4	8	20	32	12	36
9	18	45	72	27	81
7	14	35	56	21	63

2 Hannah has a bag of strawberry and raspberry sweets. All the sweets are red.
Hannah chooses a sweet at random.
Write whether each of these outcomes are certain, possible or impossible.
a Hannah chooses a red sweet. *Certain*
b Hannah chooses a raspberry sweet. *possible*
c Hannah chooses a lemon sweet. *impossible*

3 Match each pink event card with one blue probability card.

When you toss a coin you will get a head or a tail	When you roll a normal dice you will get a 7	When you pick a card from a pack you will get an ace

Impossible	Possible	Certain

4 Sandra rolls a normal six-sided dice.
Choose a word from the cloud to describe the probability of these outcomes.
a Sandra rolls a 6. *Unlikely*
b Sandra rolls an odd number. *even chance*
c Sandra rolls a number bigger than 1. *likely*
d Sandra rolls a number less than 7. *certain*
e Sandra rolls a 10. *impossible*

> likely   impossible   certain   even chance   unlikely

5 Here is a darts board.
Abu throws a dart at the board.
a Which colour is the dart most likely to land on? *red*
b Which colour is the dart least likely to land on? *yellow*

6 Copy this probability scale.

Impossible — Even — Certain

Mark each of these outcomes on the scale.
a When you take a card from a pack it will be a diamond. *even*
b It will rain in Edinburgh in December. *certain*
c Someone in your class ate breakfast today. *certain*
d When you toss a coin you will get a head. *even*
e Tomorrow is August 40th. *even*

5.5 Probability in numbers

1 Write down all the square numbers from this grid.

32	1	17	8	24	64	20	2
10	19	37	47	4	61	12	25
36	5	41	22	58	39	45	63
35	21	9	11	15	16	51	23

2 Copy this probability scale.

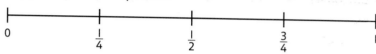

Graham spins the spinner.
Mark each of these outcomes on the scale.

a The spinner lands on red. 4/7

b The spinner lands on blue. 2/7

c The spinner lands on pink. 0

d The spinner lands on red, blue or green. 7/7

3 Mandy is a member of 'The Havens' football team.
'The Havens' play a match against 'The Stars' football team.
List all the possible outcomes for 'The Havens'.
They loose They win.

4 Derek plays for a rugby team.
They have two matches left to play in the league competition.
List all the possible outcomes for the last two matches.
½ ½

5 Dai has a bag of counters.
There are 3 blue counters, 2 orange counters,
4 pink counters and 1 green counter.
Dai chooses one counter at random.
Work out the probability of getting

a a blue counter? 3/10

b an orange counter? 2/10

c a pink counter? 4/10

d a green counter? 1/10

6 A box of chocolates contains milk chocolates and white chocolates.
The probability of picking a milk chocolate is $\frac{2}{3}$.
What is the probability of not picking a milk chocolate? 1/3

7 The probability of Paul winning a squash game is 0.6
What is the probability of Paul losing a squash game? 0.4
(Note: a squash game cannot be drawn.)

5.6 I'm a mathematician, get me out of here!

1 The pink cards are question cards. The yellow cards are answer cards.
Match each pink card with the correct yellow card.

| 35 | Double 4 to get | 21 | Half of 70 is | Double 12 to get | 8 |

| Half of 18 is | 24 | Double 16 to get | 9 | Half of 42 is | 32 |

2 Look at these two newspaper articles.

Newspaper A

Didier Deschamps has revealed he would relish the exciting test of reviving Newcastle's fortunes after he swept ahead of Mark Hughes and fellow Frenchman Gerard Houllier to emerge as the front runner in the race to be the club's next manager. Deschamps, who captained France to their World Cup final victory over Brazil, was sacked by Jueventus last May, then turned down the Manchester City job.

Newspaper B

There is no bigger hero at Newcastle than Alan Shearer. He has not yet kicked a ball for them in two years, but he is still held in the same regard as when he donned the famous black and white number nine shirt. In a decade he may not have brought the silverware the fans craved, but they came ever so close and the faithful could always dream. Now many of them dream of him returning to save the club as manager.

a Copy and complete this frequency table, one for **each** newspaper article.
Make a tally of the number of letters in each word.
Didier, which has 6 letters, and Deschamps, which has 9 letters, have been done for you.

Number of letters in word	Tally	Frequency
1		
2		
3		
4		
5		
6	I	
7		
8		
9	I	
10		

b Draw a bar chart of your results, one for each newspaper article.

3 Use your results in Q2 to answer these questions.
  a Which newspaper article uses longer words? Newspaper B
  b What is the most common length of word used in each newspaper article?
  c What is the probability of a 10-letter word occurring in each newspaper article? Unlikely
  d What is the probability of an 8-letter word occurring in each newspaper article? possible

6.1 Writing expressions

1 Work out

   a 6.8×100 680   **b** 19.3×1000 19300   **c** $27.8 \div 10$ 2.78 ✓

   d $7.4 \div 100$ 0.74   0.074 ✗   **e** 0.125×100 12.5 ✓   **f** $17.2 \div 1000$ 0.0172 ✓

2 Bianca has c coins in her pocket.
Write an expression for the number of coins in her pocket when

   a she takes two coins out $c - 2$ ✓

   b she puts four coins in. $c + 4$ ✓

3 Bridget is t cm tall.
Write an expression for the height of her friends.

   a Bali is 5cm shorter than Bridget. $t - 5cm$ ✓

   b Bardo is $\frac{1}{2}$ cm taller than Bridget. $t + \frac{1}{2}$ ✓

4 Bill has p posters and Bruce has 6 posters.
How many posters do they have altogether? $p + 6$ ✓

5 Bryn's dog is l cm long.
Write an expression for the length of his friend's dogs.

   a Chris's dog is 30 cm longer than Bryn's dog. $l + 30$ ✓

   b Daren's dog is 15 cm shorter than Bryn's dog. $l - 15$ ✓

   c Esta's dog is twice as long as Bryn's dog. $l \times 2 = 2l$ ✓

   d Fleur's dog is half as long as Bryn's dog. $l - \frac{1}{2} \times \frac{1}{2}l$

6 The mystery number is n.
Write expressions for these amounts.

   a Twice as much as the number. $n \times 2 = 2n$ ✓

   b Five more than the number in part **a**. $n \times 2 \times 5 \times 2n + 5$

   c The number shared by 3. $n \div 3$ ✓

   d 12 shared by the number. $12 \div n$ ✓

   e Five times the number then 10 is subtracted. $(n \times 5) - 10$ ✓

   f The number squared then divided by 2. $n^2 \div 2$ ✓

7 The first mystery number is x. The second mystery number is y.
Write expressions for the following amounts.

   a Three times the first number added to the second number.

   b Twice the sum of the two numbers.

   c The first number added to 10 times the second number and the result squared.

5c   5c   5c   5b   5a   5a

6.2 Order of operations

1 Write down the value of the 3 in each of these numbers.

a 9366 *hundreths* b 18.32 *tenths* c 28573 *Units* d 71.43 *Units*

2 Sebastian has done his homework.
He is not very good at BIDMAS questions.
Check his homework and correct any mistakes.

a $3 \times 7 + 2 = 23$ ✓   b $3 + 7 \times 2 = 20$ *7×3 = (21)*   c $12 \div 4 + 2 = 2$ *3+2 = (5)*

d $12 + 4 \div 2 = 8$ e $20 - 8 \times 2 = 24$ *16 = 20 = (-4)*   f $4 \times 6 + 2 = 26$ ✓

3 Calculate:

a $2 \times 8 - 3 \times 5$ *1*   b $3 + 2 \times 3 - 7$ *8*   c $1 \times 1 + 1 + 1$ *3*

d $4 + 1 \times 2 \times 3$ *30*   e $5 + 10 \div 2 + 1$ *8.5*   f $2 \times 5 + 12 \div 6$ *3.6*

4 Calculate:

a $(3 + 4) \times 5$ b $3 \times 4 - 5$ c $3 \times (4 + 5)$

d $2 \times 3 + 4 \times 5$ e $200 + 3 \times (40 - 5)$ f $\dfrac{(200 + 300)}{4 \times 5}$

5 Calculate:

a $3^2 \times 2 \times 10$ b $10^2 + 18$ c $(18 - 14)^2 - 12$

d $(35 - 5^2) \div 5$ e $(1^2 + 2^2) \times (7^2 - 6^2)$ f $3^2(10 - 4) - 4$

6 Put brackets into these calculations to make them correct.

a $1 + 2 + 3^2 = 36$ b $1 + 2 + 3^2 = 26$ c $1 + 2 + 3^2 = 12$

d $8 - 2^2 + 5 = 41$ e $7^2 - 4 - 3 = 48$ f $5 + 5^2 \div 5 - 1 = 5$

7 To work out 6×43 you can use the distributive law:

$6 \times 43 = 6 \times (40 + 3) = 6 \times 40 + 6 \times 3 = 240 + 18 = 258$

Use this method to calculate:

a 5×31 *115*   b 3×45 *135*   c 8×32 *256*   d 4×245 *100*

6.3 Simplifying expressions

1 Fill in the missing digits in these calculations.

   a _ _ _ × 10 = 1550   **b** 740_ ÷ 10 = _40   **c** 91_0 ÷ 10 = _ _7

2 Simplify these expressions by collecting like terms.

   a $a + a + a + a$ **b** $3b + 5b - 4b - b$ **c** $c + 2c + 3c + 4c - 10c$

   d $3d + 3 + 2d + 2$ **e** $6e + 2 - 3e - 3$ **f** $3f - 3 + 2 - 6f$

3 Copy and complete these addition pyramids.

a 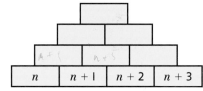   **b**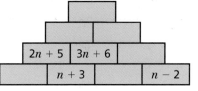

4 Find the perimeter of each shape.
Simplify your expressions.

a 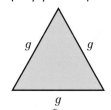   **b** 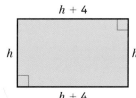   **c**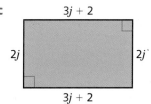

5 Simplify these expressions by collecting like terms.

   a $k + k + k + l + l$ **b** $m + n + m + n + m - n + m$

   c $3p + 5q + 2p - q$ **d** $3r + 2s + 9 - r + 5s - 2$

6 Copy and complete this addition pyramid.

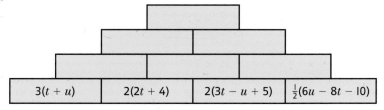

7 Find the perimeter of each shape.
Simplify your expressions.

a 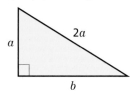   **b** 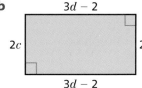   **c**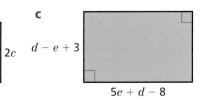

6.4 Substituting into formulae

1 Put the correct sign, > or <, between each pair of numbers.

   a 3.75 ☐ 3.9   **b** 64.45 ☐ 46.54

   c 30p ☐ £0.41   **d** − 2.1°C ☐ 1.1°C

2 Sheena runs an engraving service.
She works out how much to charge her customers using this word formula:
cost in pence = number of letters × 10 + 400
How much would it cost for the following:

   a an engraving 6 letters long?

   b an engraving 50 letters long?

3 The cost of petrol for a journey can be worked out using this formula:
cost in pounds = price per litre × number of litres used
Work out the cost of a journey when:

   a one litre of petrol costs £0.90 and 20 litres are used

   b one litre of petrol costs £0.96 and 45 litres are used

4 The formula to find the area of a triangle is:

   area = $\frac{1}{2}$ × base × height

Find the area of these triangles.

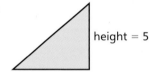

   a height = 6, base = 10   **b** height = 5, base = 6

5 $a = 2$, $b = 3$, $c = 4$, $d = 5$. Find the value of:

   a $3b$ **b** $a + d$ **c** bc **d** $40 - c$

   e $\frac{1}{4}c$ **f** $a + b + c - d$ **g** abc **h** $5b - 3d$

6 $a = 2$, $b = 3$, $c = 4$, $d = 5$. Find the value of:

   a $100 - cd$ **b** $d^2 + 3b$ **c** $c^2 - 2ab$

   d $3a^2 + b^2$ **e** $\frac{1}{2}d + 2b^2$ **f** $c^2 - d^2$

7 The formula for converting a temperature C in degrees Celsius (°C), to temperature F in degrees Fahrenheit (°F) is

   $F = (9C + 160) \div 5$

Work out these temperatures in degrees Fahrenheit.

   a The boiling point of pure water is 100°C.

   b The freezing point of pure water is 0°C.

   c The normal body temperature of a human is 37°C.

4a
4a
4a
5c
5b
5b

Play any game on the LiveText CD

6.5 Deriving formulae

1 Cordell worked out £7.55 plus 75p on his calculator.

The display showed [82.55]

What did Cordell do wrong? *Nothing*

2 a The number of coloured pencils in a pencil case is 12 more than the number of pens.
How many coloured pencils will there be if there are
i 2 pens? *14* **ii** 6 pens? *18* **iii** 1 pen? *13*

b Write a formula for the number of coloured pencils if the number of pens is p. *P+12*

3 a Amy has 200 free texts at the start of each month.
How many texts will she have left if she sends
i 150 texts? *50* **ii** 20 texts? *180* **iii** 100 texts? *100*

b Write a formula for the number of texts left if Amy sends y texts. *200-y*

4 a Paulo tiles his bathroom. He uses five times the number of white tiles than green tiles.
How many white tiles does he need to go with
i 20 green tiles? *100* **ii** 50 green tiles? *250* **iii** 7 green tiles? *40*

b Write a formula for the number of white tiles if Paulo uses t green tiles. *t×5*

5 a Inga only gets sparrows and greenfinches on her bird table.
Work out the total number of birds on her bird table when there are
i 6 sparrows and 4 greenfinches *10*
ii 12 sparrows and 2 greenfinches *14*
iii 3 sparrows and 9 greenfinches. *12*

b Write a formula for the total number of birds on Inga's bird table when there are s sparrows and g greenfinches *S+g*

6 Shaun converts miles into kilometres by multiplying the number of miles by 8, then dividing by 5.

a Use this method to convert 10 miles into kilometres. *16*

b Write a formula to convert m miles into kilometres. *M×8÷5*

7 A football team gets 3 points for winning a game, 1 point for a drawing a game and 0 points for losing a game.

a How many points does a team get if it wins 12 games, draws 6 games and loses 7 games? *×3=36 42*

b Write a formula for the number of points a team gets if it wins w games, draws d games and loses l games? *W+3 d+1 L+0*

5c

5c

5b

5b

5a

5a

7.1 Angles and lines

1 Copy and complete these calculations using complements to 100.

   a 27 + ___ = 100   **b** 71 + ___ = 100   **c** ___ + 48 = 100

2 In the diagram, ∠DCB is a right angle.

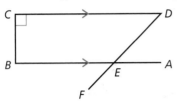

   a Which of these angles is a right angle like ∠DCB?

     i ∠BED   **ii** ∠EBC   **iii** ∠DEA   **iv** ∠FEA

   b Which line is parallel to BA? CD

   c Which line is perpendicular to BA? DF

3

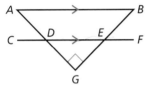

   a Which of the angles is a right angle? AGB

   b Which line is parallel to DE? AB

   c Which line is perpendicular to BG? GB

4

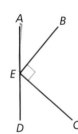

   a What type of angle is ∠CEB? right angle

   b ∠CED is 40°. Work out ∠AEB. 140°

5

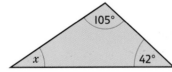

Work out angle *x*. 33°

$$\begin{array}{r} 105 \\ +\ 42 \\ \hline 147 \end{array} \qquad \begin{array}{r} 1\overset{7}{\cancel{8}}\overset{1}{\cancel{0}} \\ -\ 147 \\ \hline 033 \end{array}$$

6

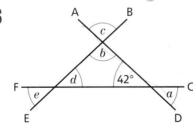

The lines AD and BE are perpendicular.
Find the size of each angle *a* to *e*. 84°

7.2 Properties of triangles and quadrilaterals

1 Work out

a $\begin{array}{r} 372 \\ + 855 \\ \hline 1227 \end{array}$ b $\begin{array}{r} 878 \\ + 252 \\ \hline 1130 \end{array}$ c $\begin{array}{r} 593 \\ - 141 \\ \hline 452 \end{array}$ d $\begin{array}{r} 782 \\ - 286 \\ \hline 496 \end{array}$

2 Write down whether each triangle is scalene, isosceles or equilateral.

a  isoseles b isoseles c  isodes d 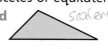 scalene e 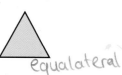 equalateral

3 Name each shape from its description.
  a I have three sides and all my angles are different. Scalene
  b I have less than five sides and all of my sides are equal. equalateral
   I have more than two angles of 90°. isoseles

4 Copy this diagram three times.
  a On your first diagram mark an acute angle.
  b On your second diagram mark an obtuse angle.
  c On your third diagram mark a reflex angle.
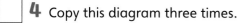

5 a Sketch a triangle for each set of angles below.
  b Label the triangles as scalene, isosceles or equilateral.
   i 60°, 40°, 80°   **ii** 60°, 60°, 60°   **iii** 70°, 100°, 10°   **iv** 70°, 55°, 55°
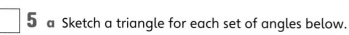

6 Write true or false for each of these statements.
If the statement is true, draw a sketch.
If the statement is false, explain why.
  a It is possible to draw a triangle with an acute angle and an obtuse angle. false
  b It is possible to draw a triangle with a reflex angle. true
  c It is possible to draw an isosceles triangle with a right angle. true
  d It is possible to draw a scalene triangle with a right angle. false
  e It is possible to draw a scalene triangle with an obtuse angle. true
  f It is possible to draw a triangle with the shortest side opposite the biggest angle. true

7 Write true or false for each of these statements.
If the statement is true, draw a sketch.
If the statement is false, explain why.
  a It is possible to draw a quadrilateral with two obtuse angles. false
  b It is possible to draw a quadrilateral with three obtuse angles. false
  c It is possible to draw a quadrilateral with three acute angles. true
  d It is possible to draw a quadrilateral with four acute angles. true
  e It is possible to draw a quadrilateral with one reflex angle. false

 3c
 4c
 4b
 4a
 5c
 5b

7.3 Using coordinates

1 Write these temperatures in order, coldest first.

−8°C, 9°C, 0°C, −2°C, 1°C   *−8, −2°C, 0°C, 1°C, 9°C*

2 The diagram shows part of a treasure map.
The side of each square on the grid is measured as 10 steps.

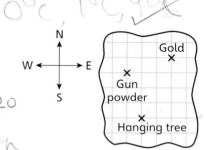

a How do you get from the Hanging Tree to the Gold?   *take 40 steps north and 20 steps east*

b How do you get from the Gold to the Gunpowder?   *30 steps west 10 steps south*

3 The diagram shows the position of two squares.
Write down the coordinates of the points A to G.

A = (8, 2) b = (8, 8) c = (2, 8)
d = (5, 4) e (6, 5) f = (5, 6)
G (4, 5)

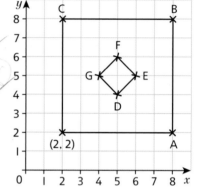

4 Draw a grid the same size as in Q3.
Plot these coordinates on the grid and join each in turn with a straight line.

(0, 0)   (8, 0)   (0, 4)   (8, 4)   (4, 8)   (0, 4)   (0, 0)   (8, 4)   (8, 0)

5 Write down the coordinates of the point halfway between

a (1, 2) and (1, 6)   **b** (−2, 4) and (−2, −4)   **c** (−3, −2) and (5, 1)

6 The diagram shows a square spiral, getting bigger.

a Write down the coordinates of the points marked with crosses. *(−2, 2), (2, 2) (2, 1)*
(1, 1) (1, 2)

b Write down the coordinates of the next four points in the shape.

① (−2, 1) ② (−2, −2) ③ (2, −2)
④ (2, 3) See me about Q. 6

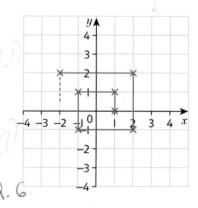

7 The line BD is a diagonal of the rectangle ABCD.

a Copy a blank grid like the one in Q6.
Plot and join the points B(−2, −3) and D(0, 3)

b Find the mid-point of the line BD

c Use this to help you draw in the other diagonal of the rectangle.

d There are two possible sets of whole number coordinates for A and C.
Write down one set.

8.1 Planning data collection

1 John buys a pair of shoes for £32.75, a pair of jeans for £18.99, and a T-shirt for £6.49
   a Use your calculator to work out the total cost. *£58.23*
   b John paid with three £20 notes.
   How much change did he receive? *£1.77*

2 Select the most appropriate metric units to use when collecting this data.
   a The distance each member of a cricket team can throw a ball. *metres*
   b How long each of your friends can hold their breath. *seconds / minutes*
   c Capacity of a car's petrol tank. *litres*
   d The mass of Year 11 pupils. *kg*

3 Nadia wants to find out if people over the age of 20 enjoy playing sport.
   She decides to ask about 30 people who look at least 20 years old.
   She decides to stand outside her local sports centre.
   Will this survey provide fair information? *No, because she's picking people that look 20 years old.*

4 How could you collect this data?
   a The number of times an ace is picked when you choose a card at random from a pack of cards. *Frequency table*
   b The number of goals scored by your school's netball team last year. *Frequency table*
   c The favourite subject of your classmates. *Frequency table.*

5 Maggie wants to do something for charity.
   She wants to find out whether a disco or a fashion show would be more popular with the sixth form.
   There are 300 pupils in the sixth form.
   How many of them should she ask? *150*

6 a How many times should you carry out
   i an experiment to test whether Year 8 pupils know that $8^2 = 64$?
   ii an experiment to test whether you get a total of 7 when you roll two dice?
   b How many pupils should you ask in a survey to find the average time spent playing sport by pupils in your school? *20*

7 Write suitable questions for a survey to find out this information.
   Choose the accuracy with which the answers are required.
   a The time pupils go to bed.
   b The amount of time pupils watch television on a Saturday.
   c The number of portions of fruit and vegetables that pupils ate last week.
   d The amount of maths homework that pupils think they should have.

8.2 Collecting data

1 Soo has £10 to buy 32p stamps.

   a How many stamps can he buy? *32*

   b What is the total cost? *£9.92*

   c How much change would he have? *8p*

2 Copy and complete the frequency table.

Favourite pet	Tally	Frequency
Dog	HT HT II	12
Cat	HT I	6
Horse	HT II	*7*
Goldfish	III	*3*
Mouse	III	*3*
Rat	I	*1*
Amphibian	IIII	*4*
Insect	III	3

3 Carlos kept a record of the number of goals scored by Barcelona football club in their last 20 matches. These are his results.

   0   0   1   1   1   0   0   3   2   2

   0   1   1   0   3   2   2   1   1   1

   Record this data in a frequency table.

goals scored	Tally	frequency
0	HT I	6
1	HT III	8
2	IIII	4
3	II	2

4 Roll two dice.
   I don't have a dice
   Add the scores.
   Record the result in a frequency table.
   Repeat a total of 36 times.

5 Construct a grouped frequency table to show the exam marks, out of 100, for Mr Watt's science class.

6 Construct a grouped frequency table with equal class widths to show the heights, in cm, of members of your family.

7 Use either 'discrete' or 'continuous' to describe these types of data.

   a The height of a pupil. *continuous*

   b The number of people who live in your house. *discrete*

   c The weight of an ant. *continuous*

   d The time that you can hold your breath. *discrete*

   e The number of pens in your house. *discrete*

8.3 Displaying data

1 These prices are displayed in a shop window.
Rearrange the prices, starting with the lowest.

| 75p ② | £1.20 ④ | £0.81 ③ | £0.05 ① | 140p ⑤ |

2 The pictogram shows the number of Lee's
friends that liked different holiday
destinations.

    a How many of Lee's friends liked Scotland best? 6

    b Which was the least liked holiday destination? *France*

    c How many of Lee's friends took part in the
survey? *36 friends*

England	☀ ☀ ☀ ☀
Scotland	☀ ☀ ☀
Wales	☀ ☀ ☀ ☀ ☀
France	☀ ☀
Spain	☀ ☀ ☀ ☀

Key: ☀ represents 2 friends

3a

3 The pictogram shows the number of different
computer games that Jo owns.

    a How many racing games does Jo own? 4

    b How many puzzle games does Jo own? 2

    c What do you think is Jo's favourite game?
Why do you think this? *Action because
she has 8 of them
and thats the most.*

Education	● ◖
Action	● ●
Racing	◖
Puzzles	◖

Key: ● represents 4 games

3a

4 This table shows the number of people taking part in different activities at a
sports centre.

Sport	Squash	Badminton	Swimming	Aerobics	Weight training
Number of people	4	8	13	8	10

Draw a bar chart to show this data.

4c

5 Some people were asked how many films they had watched in the last week.

Number of films	0	1	2	3	4	5
Frequency	4	17	20	6	5	1

    a How many people in total answered the question? 53

    b How many people watched four films last week? 5

    c How many people watched more than two films last week? 12

4b

6 Elisa asked 30 Year 9 pupils what level they had in their KS3 English SAT exam.
Her results were:

3	3	5	7	6	6	5	5	5	5
5	3	4	3	4	5	7	6	6	5
5	4	5	3	5	5	3	4	4	6

Record the data in a frequency table.

Result	Tally	Frequency
3	IIII	4
4	Ж╫ I	6
5	Ж╫ Ж╫ III	13
6	Ж╫	5
7	II	2

4a

8.4 Bar charts

1 The table shows the time taken to complete a jigsaw puzzle.

a Who took the longest time to complete the puzzle? HOLLY

b Write the times taken to complete the puzzle in order, quickest time first.

4.36, 4.79, 4.81, 5.69, 5.73

Name	Time (hours)
Lilly	4.36
Holly	5.73 6.13
Lawson	4.81 5.21
Penny	4.79 5.19
James	5.69 6.9

2 The table shows the shoe sizes of the pupils in Alistair's class.

Shoe size	4	5	6	7	8	9	10	11
Number of pupils	1	3	12	6	5	2	0	1

a Draw a bar-line graph to display the data.

b What is the most common shoe size in Alistair's class? 6

c How many pupils in the class had a shoe size of less than 7? 16

3 This bar-line graph shows pupils' favourite computer game.

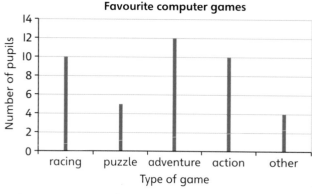

Favourite computer games

a How many pupils said that 'puzzle games' was their favourite? 5

b Which was the most popular type of game? adventure

c How many pupils took part in the survey? 43

d How many more pupils said 'racing' than 'other'? 6

4 The table shows the number of points Jim and Erek were each awarded in seven rounds of a general knowledge quiz.

Round	1	2	3	4	5	6	7
Jim	6	5	8	8	6	6	5
Erek	8	6	8	3	7	7	6

a Draw a dual bar chart to show the data.

b In which round did Jim have the biggest win over Erek? 4

c How many rounds did Erek win? 5

d Is Jim or Erek better at general knowledge? Explain your answer. Erek because he had 5 wins l out

8.5 Pie charts

1 Copy and complete these calculations.

a ◯ × 0.6 = 6   b 37 ÷ ◯◯ = 0.037   c 470 ÷ ◯ = 4.7

2 Jafar surveyed each of his classmates to find out how they travelled to school that morning.
He drew a pie chart of his results.

Travelling to school

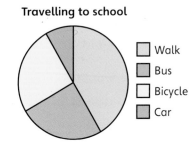

Walk
Bus
Bicycle
Car

5c

a What was the most common way to travel to school? *walk*

b What was the least common way to travel to school? *Car*

3 The pie chart shows the number of different colour cars that drove into a car park in a 10 minute period.
Five red cars drove into the car park.

Colour of car

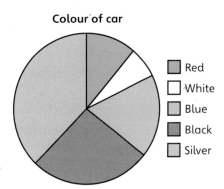

Red
White
Blue
Black
Silver

5c

a Measure the angles using a protractor.
Use the information to complete the table.

Colour	Angle	Number of cars
Red	40°	5
White	30°	3
Blue	60°	7
Black	90°	11
Silver	130°	16

b What is the total number of cars that drove into the car park in this 10 minute period? *42*

4 Ros and Mo help the environment by cleaning their local beach of litter.
These two pie charts show the types of litter they collected on their last beach clean.

5c

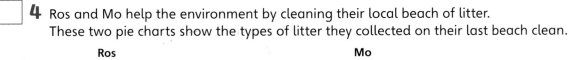

Ros   **Mo**

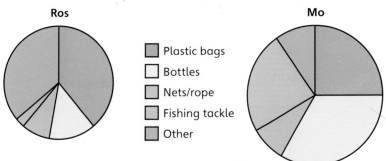

Plastic bags
Bottles
Nets/rope
Fishing tackle
Other

a Who picked up the most plastic bags? Explain your answer. *Ros, has more red*

b Mo said 'I picked up more rubbish than Ros on the last beach clean.'
Explain why Mo may be wrong. *They each have a total of each item*

c Describe the amount of nets/rope, fishing tackle and 'other' collected.
Explain each answer. *The two collected a different amount,*

9.1 Measures

1 Work out the final bank balance for each of these
   a Current balance £22, deposit £40. *£62*
   b Current balance £35, withdrawal £20. *£15*
   c Current balance £25, withdrawal £60. *£0*
   d Current balance −£18, deposit £30. *£48*

2 Which metric units would you use to measure each of these?
   a the height of a building *m*   b the mass of a dog *kg*
   c the capacity of a mug *ml*   d the length of a drawing pin *mm*
   e the mass of an apple *ml*   f the capacity of a bucket *L*

3 Put these cards in order, smallest first.

  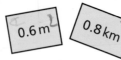

10 cm³   3 m⁶   0.6 m²   0.8 km   15 mm   370 mm⁴   250 m⁵

4 Write down the value shown on each of these scales.

a    *68 mm 61*

b 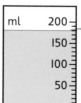   *158 ml*

c 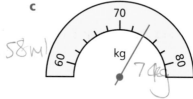   *74 kg*

5 The diagram shows a tyre pressure gauge.
   Tyre pressures are measured in psi (pounds per square inch).
   a Write down the value shown on this gauge. *32 psi*
   b Copy the tyre pressure gauge and draw arrows on it to
     show the following pressures.
     i 26 psi   **ii** 48 psi   **iii** 74 psi

6 Copy and complete these metric conversions
   a 2 kg = ___ g   b 0.8 kg = ___ g   c 3500 g = ___ kg
   d 6.2 m = ___ cm   e 25 mm = ___ cm   f 0.5 km = ___ m
   g 150 cl = ___ l   h 700 ml = ___ cl   i 4.5 l = ___ ml

7 | 1 kilogram ≈ 2.2 pounds | | 1 litre ≈ 1.75 pints |
   a Megan picks 3.5 kilograms of apples.   b Lars buys 14 pints of milk.
     Approximately how many pounds   Approximately how many litres
     is this? *8.8*   is this? *22.75*

9.2 Mental methods

1 Put these temperatures in order, smallest first.

12.6°C   15.2°C   13°C   11.9°C   12.1°C   11.3°C   15.7°C

2 Add together the numbers in each shape. Write down your answer.

a

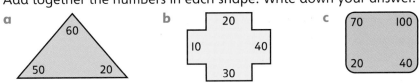

60
50   20

b
20
10   40
30

c
70   100
20   40

3c

3 The total of 6 + 2 + 8 + 5 + 4 can be found using this number bond flow chart.

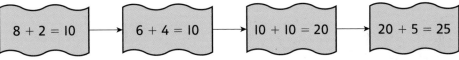

8 + 2 = 10 → 6 + 4 = 10 → 10 + 10 = 20 → 20 + 5 = 25

Draw a number bond flow chart for each of these.

a 7 + 5 + 2 + 3 + 5   b 9 + 2 + 8 + 6 + 1
c 3 + 9 + 4 + 6 + 7 + 7 + 1   d 4 + 5 + 5 + 5 + 3 + 6

3b

4 Add these batting scores mentally.

a 32, 8, 19   b 24, 5, 23
c 18, 29, 16   d 37, 11, 14

3a

5 Copy and complete this multiplication grid.

×	3	7	
4	12	28	24
2	6	14	18
	3	35	12

4c

6 Use partitioning to multiply these.

a 26 × 3   b 34 × 7   c 51 × 8   d 48 × 4

4c

7 Copy and complete this number pyramid.
The number in each brick can be found
by adding the two bricks below it.
Use whole number calculations to
help you with these.

31 + 14 = 45
3.1 + 1.4 = 4.5

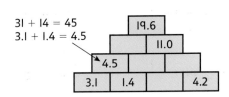

19.6
11.0
4.5
3.1   1.4   4.2

4b

8 Use a calculator to work these out. Check your answers by working backwards.

a 3.6 ÷ 5   b 2415 ÷ 35

4a

9.3 Endangered isle

1 Write **true** or **false** for each of these.

   a 5 is a factor of 30.   **b** 12 is a multiple of 8.

   c 9 is a prime number.   **d** $\frac{1}{4} + \frac{1}{4} = \frac{2}{8}$

   e 25 is a square number.   **f** $100 - 42 = 68$

   g The next term in the sequence 4, 7, 10, 13 ... is 16.

   h The next term in the sequence 38, 30, 22, 14, ... is 8.

2 Arrange these cards into groups that give the same answer.

$5 + 5 + 5 + 5$ $48 \div 2$ $8 + 8$ 6×4 2×10 $32 \div 2$

8×3 $12 + 12$ 4×5 $8 + 8 + 8$ $48 \div 3$ $40 \div 2$ 2×8

3 Find the missing numbers in each of these.

   a $2 \times 13 \times 5 = 2 \times \boxed{} \times 13 = \boxed{} \times 13 = \boxed{}$

   b $2 \times 8 \times 4 = 2 \times 4 \times 8 = \boxed{} \times 8 = \boxed{}$

   c $5 \times 7 \times 8 = 5 \times \boxed{} \times 7 = \boxed{} \times 7 = \boxed{}$

   d $\frac{1}{2} \times 23 \times 6 = \frac{1}{2} \times 6 \times \boxed{} = 3 \times \boxed{} = \boxed{}$

4 Copy this table.

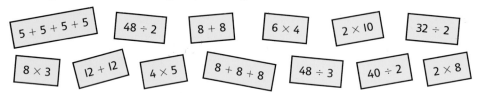

question	working: step 1	working: step 2	answer
a 12 × 40	3 × 5 × 6	35 × 10	90
b 15 × 6	8 × 7 × 2	48 × 10	112
c 5 × 36	12 × 4 × 10	10 × 18	350
d 8 × 14	7 × 2 × 5 × 5	3 × 30	180
e 14 × 25	5 × 2 × 18	56 × 2	480

Draw a line linking the question on the left, to the two steps of working in the middle, to the answer on the right.
The first one is done for you.

5 Copy and complete these.

   a $4 \times 63 = 4 \times (60 + 3)$
             $= 4 \times 60 + 4 \times \underline{}$
             $= 240 + \underline{}$
             $= \underline{}$

   b $8 \times 92 = 8 \times (90 + \underline{})$
             $= 8 \times 90 + 8 \times \underline{}$
             $= 720 + \underline{}$
             $= \underline{}$

   c $6 \times 59 = 6 \times (60 - 1)$
             $= 6 \times 60 - 6 \times \underline{}$
             $= 360 - \underline{}$
             $= \underline{}$

   d $7 \times 38 = 7 \times (40 - \underline{})$
             $= 7 \times 40 - 7 \times \underline{}$
             $= 280 - \underline{}$
             $= \underline{}$

4C

9.4 Rounding

1 Copy and complete these multiplication and division facts.

a $6 \times 7 = 42$ $42 \div 6 = 7$ $42 \div 7 = 6$

b $8 \times 3 = 24$ $24 \div 3 = 8$ $24 \div 8 = 3$

c $4 \times 9 = 36$ $36 \div 9 = 4$ $36 \div 4 = 9$

d $5 \times 6 = 30$ $30 \div 5 = 6$ $30 \div 6 = 5$

2 Round these numbers to the nearest 10.

a 84 80   b 45 50   c 762 760   d 909 910   e 2315 2320

3 Round these numbers to the nearest 100.

a 476 500   b 778 800   c 250 300   d 1230 1200   e 2990 3000

4 Round the numbers on the blue cards to the nearest 1000.
Find the correct answer on the red card. Write down the matching pairs.

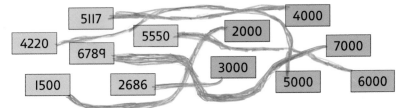

5 Use rounding to estimate the answer to these calculations.
Find the exact answer using a calculator and compare your results.

a $7.8 + 48.8$ 57   b $69.8 - 32.1$ 38   c 4.2×8.9 13   d $7.95 \div 3.99$ 2

6 This table shows the number of people living in four European countries in 2002.
Round the population figures to the accuracy shown.

Country	Population	Round to the nearest	Answer
Italy	58 147 733	10 million	a
Greece	10 706 291	1 million	b
Malta	397 499	100 000	c
Andorra	68 403	1000	d

7 This table shows the area of the three largest oceans in the world.

Choose whether A, B or C is the correct answer to each of these.

Ocean	Area in km²
Pacific	169 200 000
Atlantic	106 400 000
Indian	73 556 000

a The area of the Pacific Ocean to the nearest 10 million km² is
   A 170 000 000 km²   B 169 000 000 km²   C 160 000 000 km²

b The area of the Atlantic Ocean to the nearest 1 million km² is
   A 110 000 000 km²   B 107 000 000 km²   C 106 000 000 km²

c The area of the Indian Ocean to the nearest 100 000 km² is
   A 74 000 000 km²   B 73 600 000 km²   C 73 500 000 km²

9.5 Written multiplication

1 In this number wheel opposite numbers are equal.
Copy the wheel and fill in the missing numbers.

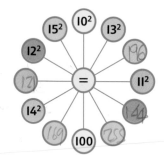

Wheel labels: 15^2, 10^2, 13^2, 12^2, 196, 121, =, 11^2, 14^2, 144, 169, 100, 225

2 Copy and complete these multiplications using the grid method.
Estimate the answers first.

a 596 × 3 *1788* Estimate = 600 × 3 = 1800

×	500	90	6
3	1500	270	18

1500   1770
+ 270 + 18
1770   1788

b 237 × 8 *1896* Estimate = 200 × 8 = 1600

×	200	30	7
8	1600	240	56

1600   1840
+ 240 + 56
1840   1896

3 Copy and complete these multiplications using the standard method.
Estimate the answers first.

a 149 × 4

Estimate = 100 × 4 = 400

$$\begin{array}{r} 1\ 4\ 9 \\ \times \quad 4 \\ \hline 6 2 6 \end{array}$$

b 382 × 6

Estimate = 400 × 6 = 2400

$$\begin{array}{r} 3\ 8\ 2 \\ \times \quad 6 \\ \hline 2 2 9 2 \end{array}$$

4 Sally keeps chickens.
She gets, on average, 3 eggs per day.
How many eggs should Sally get during 1 year (365 days)? *1095 eggs per year*
Estimate the answer first. *3 × 400 = 1200*

actual awnser:
$$\begin{array}{r} 3 6 5 \\ \times \quad 3 \\ \hline 1095 \end{array}$$

5 Marta works out 26 × 39 using the grid method.
This is the working she does.

×	20	6
30	60	180
9	180	54

60 + 180 + 180 + 54 = 474

a Which part of Marta's working is wrong? *adding*

b Work out the correct answer to 26 × 39. *1014*

180   240   420
+ 60 + 180 + 54
240   420   474

6 Gareth goes on a walking holiday.
He walks, on average, 28 km every day.
He walks for 12 days.
Work out the total distance he walks. *336km*
Estimate the answer first. *20 × 10 = 200*

×	20	8
10	200	80
2	40	16

200   280   320
+ 80   + 40   + 16
280   320   336

7 Use the written method of your choice to do these multiplications.
Estimate the answer first.

a 215 × 29 *6235* b 652 × 37 *24124* c 836 × 51 *42636*

9.6 Multiplying decimals

1 The stars show some fractions and their equivalent decimals.

Match the fractions with the equivalent decimals.

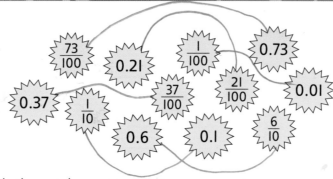

2 Copy the grid and use it to multiply the numbers.
Estimate the answer first.

a 4.3 × 8

Estimate = $\underline{4}$ × $\underline{8}$ = $\underline{32}$

×	4	0.3
8	32	2.4

32 + 2.4 = 34.6

b 2.7 × 5

Estimate = $\underline{2}$ × $\underline{5}$ = $\underline{10}$

×	2	0.7
5	10	4.0

10 + 4.0 = 5.0

c 9.4 × 3

Estimate = $\underline{9}$ × $\underline{3}$ = $\underline{27}$

×	9	0.4
3	27	1.2

27 + 1.2 = 3.9

5b

3 Copy the grid and use it to multiply the numbers.
Estimate the answer first.

a 2.15 × 5

Estimate = $\underline{2}$ × $\underline{5}$ = $\underline{10}$

×	2	0.1	0.05
5	10	0.5	0.25

10.00 + 0.5 + 0.25 = 10.5 ... 1.5

b 3.76 × 4

Estimate = $\underline{3}$ × $\underline{4}$ = $\underline{12}$

×	3	0.7	0.06
4	12	2.8	0.24

12 + 2.8 + 0.24 = 4.0 ... 0.24

c 8.27 × 3

Estimate = $\underline{8}$ × $\underline{3}$ = $\underline{24}$

×	8	0.2	0.07
3	24	0.6	0.21

24 + 0.6 + 0.21 = 0.21 / 3.0 / 3.21

5b

4 238 × 7 = 1666

Use this fact to match a blue question card with a pink answer card.

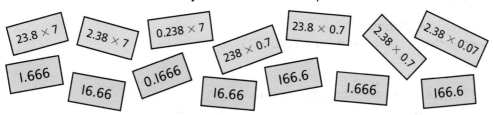

5a

5 Copy and complete these multiplications using the standard method.

a 4.9 × 5

```
  ⁴4 9
×    5
  245
```

Answer = 24.5

b 0.32 × 7

```
 ¹3 2
×   7
 224
```

Answer = 2.24

c 2.73 × 9

```
 ⁶²7 3
×    9
 2557
```

Answer = 25.57

d 43.6 × 6

```
 ²³4 3 6
×      6
 2616
```

Answer = 261.6

5a

6 This table shows the cost of photograph prints.

a David orders 6 of the 20cm × 20cm prints.
Work out the total cost for David. 1.26 × 6 = 7.59

£7.59

b Carlos orders 9 of the 30cm × 25cm prints.
Work out the total cost for Carlos. 2.79 × 9

£25.11

Size of print	Cost per print
20 cm × 20 cm	£1.29
20 cm × 25 cm	£1.89
30 cm × 25 cm	£2.79

5a

9.7 Written division

1 This is a CCC (Calculator Challenge Curve). Copy the curve.
Start at the first calculation and use a calculator to fill in the missing values.

3904 ÷ 244 = ⟨16⟩ × 96 = ⟨154⟩ + 264 = ⟨1800⟩ ÷ 25 = ⟨72⟩ − 54 = ⟨20⟩² = ⟨400⟩

2 Work out these exact divisions.
a 693 ÷ 3 231   b 848 ÷ 4 212   c 129 ÷ 3 43   d 355 ÷ 5 71
e 351 ÷ 3 117   f 728 ÷ 7 242   g 936 ÷ 4 234   h 738 ÷ 6 123

3 Work out these divisions. They all have remainders.
a 461 ÷ 4 115.29   b 623 ÷ 3 207.6   c 296 ÷ 7 42.2   d 386 ÷ 5 77, 2

4 Sally packs eggs in boxes of 6.
She has 146 eggs.
a How many full boxes of eggs does Sally pack? 24
b How many eggs has she left over? 3

5 Work out these divisions.
Some of them have remainders.
Estimate the answer first.
a 276 ÷ 12   b 345 ÷ 15   c 989 ÷ 21   d 669 ÷ 19

6 A blacksmith uses 28 nails to fix the shoes onto one horse.
He has a box of 900 nails.
a How many horses can he shoe? 32
b How many nails will he have left over? 14

7 On each side of this rectangle, the numbers
in the circles multiply to give the number
in the square.
Copy and complete the rectangle.

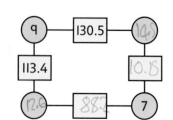

8 Four adults go to a theme park.
The total cost is £69.80.
How much does it cost per adult? £17.45

9.8 More on order of operations

1 Use these facts: $1 g = 1000\ mg$ $1\ l = 100\ cl$ $1\ cm = 10\ mm$

Work out the following:

a 2500 mg = _____ g   b 75 mm = _____ cm   c 2.4 l = _____ cl

d 0.45 g = _____ mg   e 46cl = _____ l   f 13.6 cm = _____ mm

2 Do these calculations on a calculator.
Work from left to right.

a $6.8 + 3.7 - 4.9$ b $4.2 \times 9.6 \div 0.2$

3 A taxi can carry 5 people.
How many taxis are needed to take 37 people to a party?

4 Work these out without using a calculator.

a $5 + 2 \times 3$ b $8 \div 2 + 9$ c $5 \times 7 + 11$

d $8 - 6 \div 2$ e $20 - 3 \times 5$ f $23 + 70 \div 10$

5 Work these out using a calculator.

a $(2 + 7) \times 13$ b $180 \div (12 - 3)$ c $8 \times (22 - 13)$

d $2.6 \times (4.9 + 3.7)$ e $(12.6 - 5.4) \div 0.9$ f $24 \div (0.9 + 2.3)$

6 The blue cards are question cards.
The yellow cards are answer cards.
Use a calculator to work out the
answers to the questions.

a Match each blue card with a
yellow card.

b Which question card hasn't got
an answer card?

c What is the answer to this question?

| 22.25 |
| 21.45 |
| $\dfrac{369.6}{38.4 - 21.9}$ |
| 21.26 |
| $6.5^2 - (12.4 + 7.6)$ |
| $171.6 \div (14.6 - 6.6)$ |
| $2.3 \times 4.6 + 8.9 \times 1.2$ |

7 In this number wheel opposite numbers are equal.
Copy the wheel and fill in the missing numbers.
Use the button on your calculator.

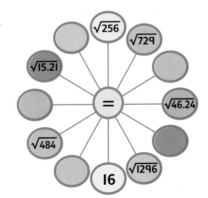

8 Write **true** or **false** for each of these.

a $\sqrt{3136} = 56$ b $\sqrt{7.2} = 3.6$ c $\sqrt{8} = 64$ d $\sqrt{361} = 19$

10.1 Multiples and factors

1 Sadiq buys a pack of three chewy bars for £1.26
   Use your calculator to work out the cost, in pence, of each bar. *42p*

2 Find all the factors of
   a 10 *2, 5, 1, 10* b 16 *4, 1, 2, 16, 8* c 18 *9, 2, 18, 1, 3, 6*
   d 21 *21, 7, 1, 3* e 35 *5, 35, 7, 1* f 40 *10, 4, 1, 40, 20, 5, 2*

3a

3 The numbers 1, 9 and 16 all have an odd number of factors.
   Write down another number that has an odd number of factors.
   21, 40, 3

3a

4 Which numbers from the cloud are
   a multiples of 6 *6*
   b multiples of 5 *25*
   c multiples of 6 and 5 *30*
   d divisible by 2 *6*
   e divisible by 5 *25*
   f divisible by 25 *100*
   g divisible by 4 *36*

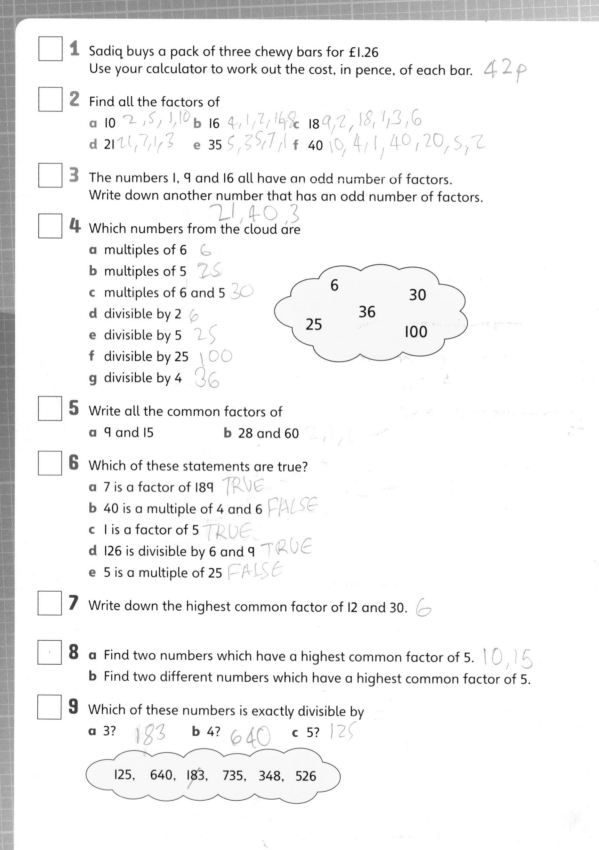

Cloud: 6, 36, 30, 25, 100

4c

5 Write all the common factors of
   a 9 and 15   b 28 and 60 *2, 1, 4*

4b

6 Which of these statements are true?
   a 7 is a factor of 189 *TRUE*
   b 40 is a multiple of 4 and 6 *FALSE*
   c 1 is a factor of 5 *TRUE*
   d 126 is divisible by 6 and 9 *TRUE*
   e 5 is a multiple of 25 *FALSE*

4a

7 Write down the highest common factor of 12 and 30. *6*

5c

8 a Find two numbers which have a highest common factor of 5. *10, 15*
   b Find two different numbers which have a highest common factor of 5.

5c

9 Which of these numbers is exactly divisible by
   a 3? *183* b 4? *640* c 5? *125*

   125, 640, 183, 735, 348, 526

4a

10.2 Generating sequences

1 This is a MCC (Mental Challenge Curve). Copy the curve.
Start at the first calculation, then in your head work out and write down the missing values.

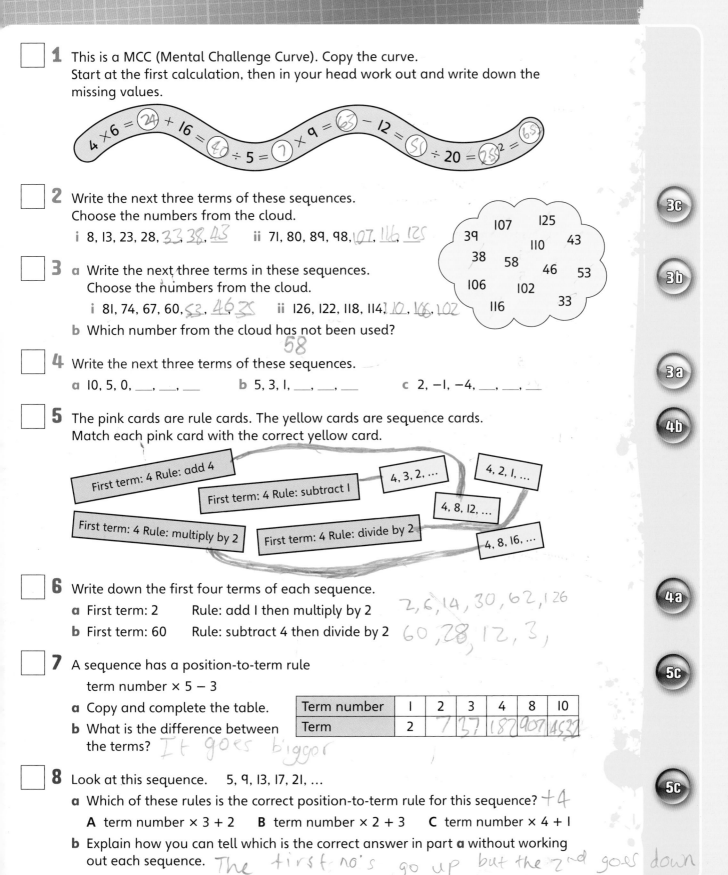

$4 \times 6 = 24$ + 16 = 40 ÷ 5 = 7 × 9 = 63 − 12 = 51 ÷ 20 = 2.5² = 6.5

2 Write the next three terms of these sequences.
Choose the numbers from the cloud.

   i 8, 13, 23, 28, 33, 38, 43   ii 71, 80, 89, 98, 107, 116, 125

Cloud: 107, 125, 39, 110, 43, 38, 58, 46, 53, 106, 102, 116, 33

3 a Write the next three terms in these sequences.
Choose the numbers from the cloud.

   i 81, 74, 67, 60, 53, 46, 39   ii 126, 122, 118, 114, 110, 106, 102

  b Which number from the cloud has not been used?
    58

4 Write the next three terms of these sequences.

  a 10, 5, 0, ___, ___, ___   **b** 5, 3, 1, ___, ___, ___   **c** 2, −1, −4, ___, ___, ___

5 The pink cards are rule cards. The yellow cards are sequence cards.
Match each pink card with the correct yellow card.

First term: 4 Rule: add 4

First term: 4 Rule: subtract 1

First term: 4 Rule: multiply by 2

First term: 4 Rule: divide by 2

4, 3, 2, ...

4, 2, 1, ...

4, 8, 12, ...

4, 8, 16, ...

6 Write down the first four terms of each sequence.

  a First term: 2   Rule: add 1 then multiply by 2   2, 6, 14, 30, 62, 126

  b First term: 60   Rule: subtract 4 then divide by 2   60, 28, 12, 3,

7 A sequence has a position-to-term rule

    term number × 5 − 3

  a Copy and complete the table.

  b What is the difference between the terms? It goes bigger

Term number	1	2	3	4	8	10
Term	2	7	37	187	907	4527

8 Look at this sequence.   5, 9, 13, 17, 21, ...

  a Which of these rules is the correct position-to-term rule for this sequence? +4

    A term number × 3 + 2   **B** term number × 2 + 3   **C** term number × 4 + 1

  b Explain how you can tell which is the correct answer in part **a** without working out each sequence. The first no's go up but the 2nd goes down

3c
3b
3a
4b
4a
5c
5c

10.3 Generating sequences using rules

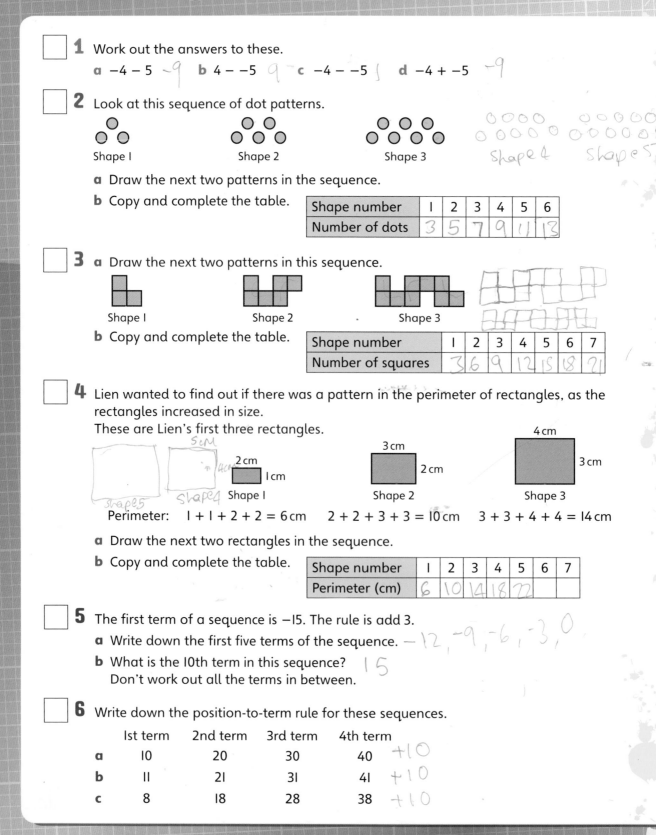

1 Work out the answers to these.

a −4 − 5 ⁻9   b 4 − −5 9   c −4 − −5 1   d −4 + −5 ⁻9

2 Look at this sequence of dot patterns.

Shape 1   Shape 2   Shape 3   Shape 4   Shape 5

a Draw the next two patterns in the sequence.

b Copy and complete the table.

Shape number	1	2	3	4	5	6
Number of dots	3	5	7	9	11	13

3 a Draw the next two patterns in this sequence.

Shape 1   Shape 2   Shape 3

b Copy and complete the table.

Shape number	1	2	3	4	5	6	7
Number of squares	3	6	9	12	15	18	21

4 Lien wanted to find out if there was a pattern in the perimeter of rectangles, as the rectangles increased in size.

These are Lien's first three rectangles.

Shape 5   Shape 4   Shape 1   Shape 2   Shape 3

Perimeter: 1 + 1 + 2 + 2 = 6 cm   2 + 2 + 3 + 3 = 10 cm   3 + 3 + 4 + 4 = 14 cm

a Draw the next two rectangles in the sequence.

b Copy and complete the table.

Shape number	1	2	3	4	5	6	7
Perimeter (cm)	6	10	14	18	22		

5 The first term of a sequence is −15. The rule is add 3.

a Write down the first five terms of the sequence. −12, −9, −6, −3, 0

b What is the 10th term in this sequence? 15
Don't work out all the terms in between.

6 Write down the position-to-term rule for these sequences.

	1st term	2nd term	3rd term	4th term	
a	10	20	30	40	+10
b	11	21	31	41	+10
c	8	18	28	38	+10

10.4 Coordinates

1 Add these fractions.

a $\frac{3}{7} + \frac{2}{7}$ $\frac{5}{7}$

b $\frac{12}{17} + \frac{1}{17}$ $\frac{13}{17}$

c $\frac{1}{6} + \frac{1}{6} + \frac{1}{6} + \frac{2}{6}$ $\frac{5}{6}$

2 The point 4C is marked by a cross.
Copy the grid and mark these points.

3D, 3E, 4F, 5F, 6F, 7E, 7D, 6C, 5C

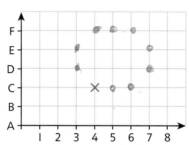

3 Copy and complete the coordinates of these letters.

A (1, $\underline{1}$)   E ($\underline{3}$, $\underline{6}$)
B ($\underline{3}$, 2)   F ($\underline{5}$, $\underline{4}$)
C ($\underline{1}$, $\underline{4}$)   G ($\underline{6}$, $\underline{2}$)
D ($\underline{0}$, $\underline{6}$)   H ($\underline{5}$, $\underline{0}$)

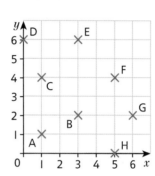

4 a Draw an x- and y-axis from 0 to 6 (as in Q3).

b Plot these coordinates.

Join them up with eight straight lines in the order they are given.

(6, 4)   (6, 2)   (4, 0)   (2, 0)   (0, 2)   (0, 4)   (2, 6)   (4, 6)   (6, 4)

c Write down the name of this shape.   hexegon

5 Copy and complete the coordinates of these letters.

A (1, $\underline{3}$)   E ($\underline{3}$, $\underline{-4}$)
B ($\underline{4}$, 2)   F ($\underline{-4}$, $\underline{1}$)
C ($\underline{2}$, $\underline{-2}$)   G ($\underline{0}$, $\underline{-1}$)
D ($\underline{-5}$, $\underline{-3}$)   H ($\underline{-1}$, $\underline{4}$)

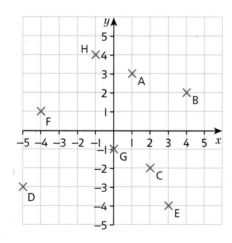

6 a Draw an x- and y-axis from −5 to 5 (as in Q5).

b Plot these coordinates.

Join them up with eighteen straight lines in the order they are given.

(−5, 4)   (−5, −4)   (−5, −1)   (−3, −1)   (−3, −4)   (0, −1)   (−2, −1)   (−2, −4)
(1, −4)   (1, 4)   (1, −4)   (2, −4)   (2, 4)   (2, −4)   (5, −4)   (5, −1)   (3, −1)   (3, −4)

c What have you written?   hello

10.5 Straight line graphs

1 Calculate

   a (3 + 6) × 2 = 18   **b** (3 + 6) ÷ 3 = 3   **c** 12 ÷ (2 + 1) 4   **d** 3 × (17 − 7) 30

2 Copy and complete the table with the coordinates shown below.

x	1	3	5	7	9
y	4	6	8	10	12

   (1, 4)   (3, 6)   (5, 8)   (7, 10)   (9, 12)

3 Write the coordinate pairs from this table.

x	4	5	6	8	10
y	2	3	4	6	8

(4, 2) (6, 4) (10, 8)
(5, 3) (8, 6)

4 Copy and complete these function machines to find the missing outputs.

   a 10 → ÷5 → 2 ; 20 → 4 ; 25 → 5 ; 50 → 10

   b 4 → −6 → −2 ; 5 → −1 ; 6 → 0 ; 10 → 4

5 Copy and complete these function machines to find the missing outputs.

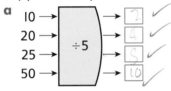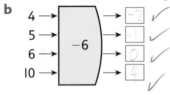

   a 10 → ×5 − 2 → 48 ; 20 → 98 ; 25 → 123 ; 50 → 248

   b 4 → +10 ÷ 2 → 7 ; 5 → 7.5 ; 6 → 8 ; 10 → 10

6 Copy and complete these tables of values for the rules given.

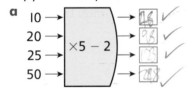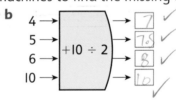

   a y = 2x

x	1	2	3	4	5
y	2	4	6	8	10

   b y = 7 − x

x	1	2	3	4	5
y	6	5	4	3	2

7 **a** Draw axes with the x-axis going from 0 to 5 and the y-axis from 0 to 10.

   b Plot the graphs for the functions in Q6.

   c Label each graph with the function.

V. Good

Play any game on the LiveText CD

11.1 Reflection symmetry

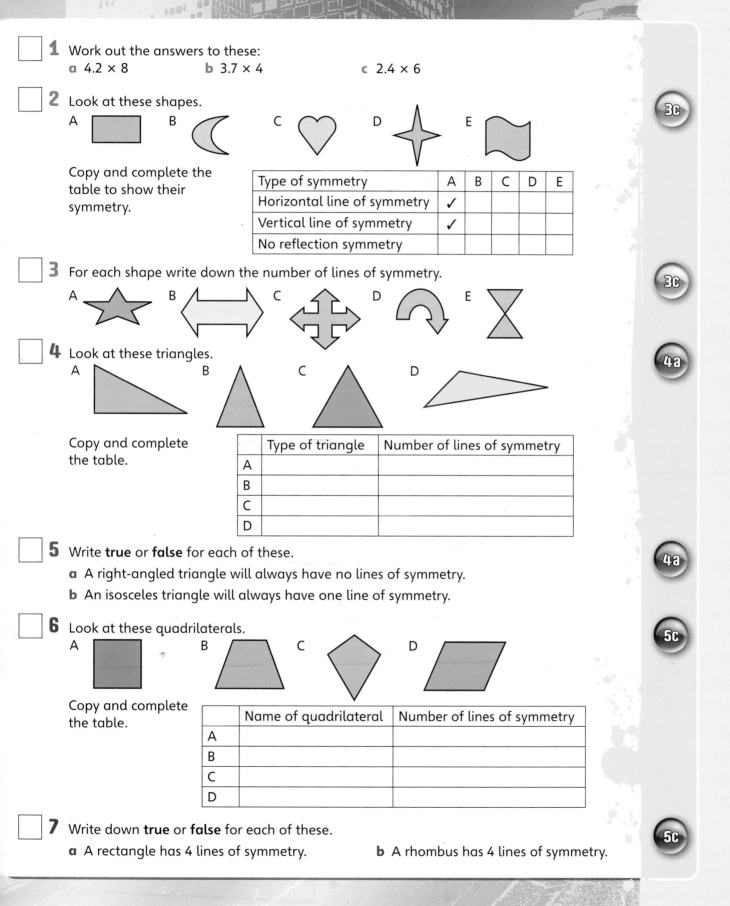

1 Work out the answers to these:
  a 4.2 × 8   **b** 3.7 × 4   **c** 2.4 × 6

2 Look at these shapes.

A   B   C   D   E

Copy and complete the table to show their symmetry.

Type of symmetry	A	B	C	D	E
Horizontal line of symmetry	✓				
Vertical line of symmetry	✓				
No reflection symmetry					

3c

3 For each shape write down the number of lines of symmetry.

A   B   C   D   E

3c

4 Look at these triangles.

A   B   C   D

Copy and complete the table.

	Type of triangle	Number of lines of symmetry
A		
B		
C		
D		

4a

5 Write **true** or **false** for each of these.
  a A right-angled triangle will always have no lines of symmetry.
  b An isosceles triangle will always have one line of symmetry.

4a

6 Look at these quadrilaterals.

A   B   C   D

Copy and complete the table.

	Name of quadrilateral	Number of lines of symmetry
A		
B		
C		
D		

5c

7 Write down **true** or **false** for each of these.
  a A rectangle has 4 lines of symmetry.   **b** A rhombus has 4 lines of symmetry.

5c

11.2 Reflection and translation

 1 Work out mentally

　a 80 + 30 + 10 + 20 　　　b 60 + 50 + 40 + 40

　c 90 + 20 + 30 + 60 　　　d 20 + 20 + 30 + 70

2 Copy these drawings.
Reflect each shape in its mirror line.

a 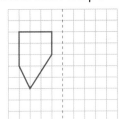　　b 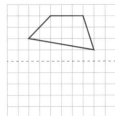　　c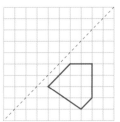

3 Look at these triangles.

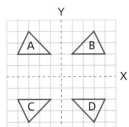

Copy and complete these sentences.
The first one is done for you.

　a Triangle A is reflected in the line X to give Triangle C

　b Triangle B is reflected in the line Y to give Triangle …

　c Triangle C is reflected in the line … to give Triangle D

　d Triangle D is reflected in the line X to give Triangle …

4 Copy these drawings and move each shape by the given amount.

a 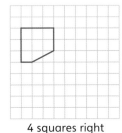　　b 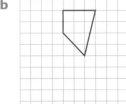　　c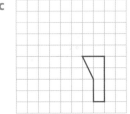

　4 squares right　　　2 squares left　　　5 squares left
　　　　　　　　　　　3 squares down　　　4 squares up

5 Look at these triangles.

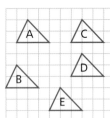

Copy and complete these sentences.
The first one is done for you.

　a Triangle A is translated to give Triangle C by moving
　　5 squares right.

　b Triangle C is translated to give Triangle D by moving …

　c Triangle D is translated to give Triangle B by moving …

　d Triangle E is translated to give Triangle A by moving …

11.3 Shapes and angle rules

1 Work out:

    a 792 ÷ 3   **b** 931 ÷ 7   **c** 639 ÷ 9   **d** 636 ÷ 6

2 In this shape, triangle BCD is a scalene triangle.
Which triangles are

    a isosceles?

    b equilateral?

    c right-angled?

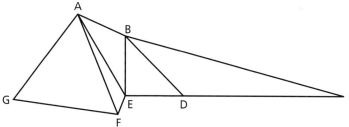

3 a What types of triangles make this shape?

    b What do the angles add up to at the centre of the shape?

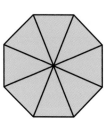

4 Calculate the missing angle in each triangle.

    a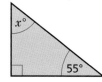

    b

    c

5 Find angle x.

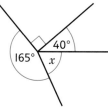

6 Look at these cards.
Match each blue card with one yellow card.

    a

Two of the angles in an isosceles triangle are 61°. The third angle is

         53°

    b

One of the angles in a right angled triangle is 37°. The third angle is

         51°

    c

The biggest angle in an isosceles triangle is 68°. The other angles are both

         58°

    d

Two of the angles in a scalene triangle are 61° and 68°. The third angles is

         56°

11.4 Drawing 2-D and 3-D shapes

1 Add these amounts

   a £8.75 + 12p   **b** 3 kg + 750 g   **c** 10.5 km + 750 m

2 Measure the height and width of this photograph to the nearest millimetre.

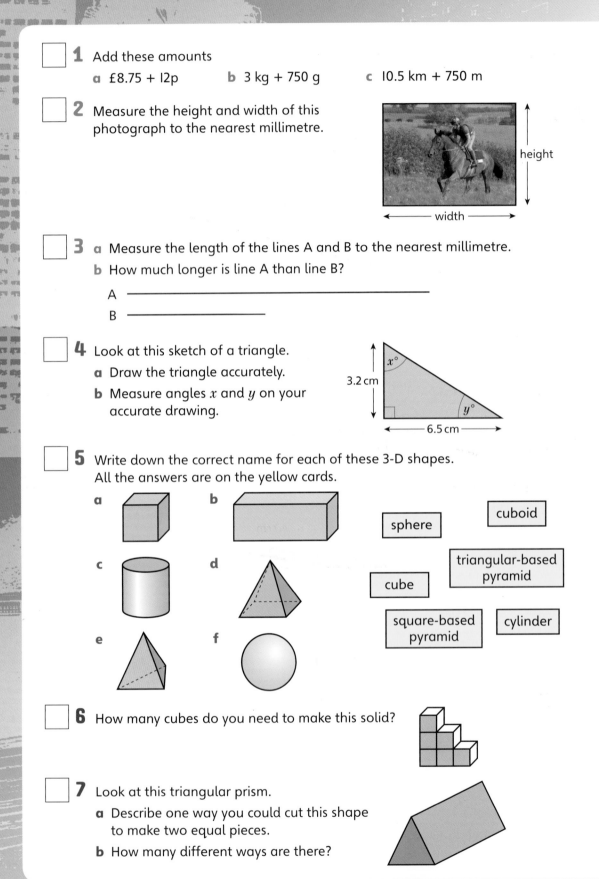

3 a Measure the length of the lines A and B to the nearest millimetre.

   b How much longer is line A than line B?

    A ———————————————————————

    B ————————————

4 Look at this sketch of a triangle.

   a Draw the triangle accurately.

   b Measure angles x and y on your accurate drawing.

    $x°$ 3.2 cm $y°$ 6.5 cm

5 Write down the correct name for each of these 3-D shapes. All the answers are on the yellow cards.

   a   **b**

   c   **d**

   e   **f**

   sphere   cuboid   triangular-based pyramid   cube   square-based pyramid   cylinder

6 How many cubes do you need to make this solid?

7 Look at this triangular prism.

   a Describe one way you could cut this shape to make two equal pieces.

   b How many different ways are there?

11.5 Constructing triangles

1 Mrs Jones car insurance costs £295.08 for 12 months.
How much is this each month?

2 Look at this diagram.
It has not been drawn accurately.

a Draw the diagram accurately.

b Measure the reflex angle $x°$.

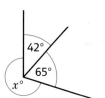

3 Measure the size of these reflex angles.

a

b

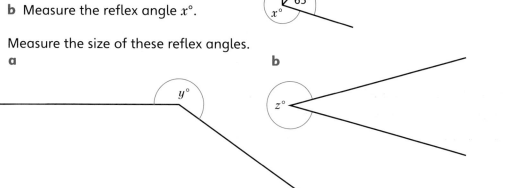

4 **a** Draw each angle between 5 cm lines.

   i 195°   **ii** 310°   **iii** 342°

b Measure the smaller angle between each pair of lines.

c Say whether each angle is acute or obtuse.

5 Draw these triangles accurately.

a

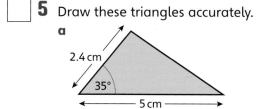

b

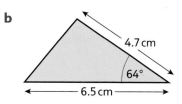

6 Draw these triangles accurately.

a

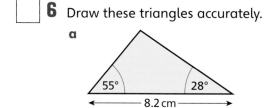

b

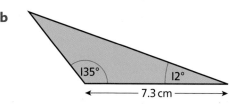

12.1 Calculating fractions

1 Mentally add these pairs of numbers.
Show your method in writing or with a diagram.

    a 47 + 23   **b** 76 + 64   **c** 88 + 97

2 Work out:

    a $\frac{3}{10} \times 40$ **b** $\frac{5}{12} \times 36$ **c** $\frac{3}{5} \times 45$

    d $\frac{4}{11} \times 77$ **e** $\frac{1}{9} \times 108$ **f** $\frac{7}{8} \times 64$

3 Copy and complete:

    a $\frac{1}{5} \times 80 = \Box$ **b** $\frac{3}{7} \times 42 = \Box$ **c** $\frac{1}{2} \times \Box = 17$ **d** $\frac{2}{3} \times \Box = 44$

4 Find the fraction answers to these:

    a $\frac{1}{3}$ of 14   **b** $\frac{4}{5}$ of 26

    c three tenths of 31 g   **d** $\frac{5}{12}$ of 49 m

5 $\frac{3}{7}$ of Tao's calculator keys are number keys.

    a What fraction of the keys are not number keys?

    There are 21 keys on Tao's calculator.

    b How many of the keys are number keys?

6 Vladimir's calculator has 45 keys.
He only knows how to use 18 of the keys.
What fraction of the keys does Vladimir know how to use?
Give your answer in its simplest form.

7 Linsey has this huge chocolate bar.

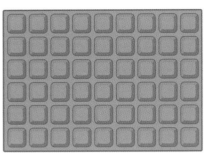

What fraction of the bar is left after Linsey eats

    a 6 pieces?   **b** 12 pieces?   **c** 22 pieces?

    d 48 pieces?   **e** 53 pieces?

Give your answers in their simplest form.

5a

5a

5a

5b

5b

5b

12.2 Fractions, decimals and percentages

1 Ashur cut 0.65 m from a 3 m length of copper pipe.
Work out the length of copper pipe left over.

2 Copy and complete this table.

Percentage	Fraction
13%	$\frac{13}{100}$
49%	
91%	
	$\frac{17}{100}$
	$\frac{83}{100}$

3 Copy and complete this table.

Percentage	Fraction	Decimal
10%		
	$\frac{1}{5}$	
		0.4
7%		
	$\frac{1}{8}$	
		0.75
140%		

4 Catrin scored 24 marks out of 40 in a science test.
   a Write this score as a fraction in its simplest form.
   b Write this score as a decimal.
   c Write this score as a percentage.

5 Lowri scored the following marks in her end of year exams.

Maths	42 out of 50	PE	17 out of 25
Science	13 out of 20	IT	3 out of 10
Spanish	4 out of 5	English	16 out of 40

   a Work out Lowri's percentage score for each subject.
   b In which subject did Lowri get her highest percentage score?

6 Convert these percentages into fractions.
Write each fraction in its simplest form.
   a 18%   **b** 36%   **c** 72%   **d** 88%   **e** 92%

12.3 Percentages of amounts

1 Write this set of measurements in order, starting with the smallest.

| 146 cm | 1.4 m | 2375 mm | 1 m 38 cm | 1.47 m |

2 a Copy this table.

```
                                    8 m
        40 m                        16 m
        £12                         10 m
        £10                         £2.50
        32 m                        £3.50
        £20                         £3
                                    £5
```

b Find 25% of the amounts in the left column.
Draw a line from these amounts to the correct answers in the right column.
The first one has been done for you.

3 A pot contains 120 g of yoghurt. 10% of the yoghurt is fat.
How many grams of fat are there in the yoghurt?

4 A large bucket of popcorn weighs 640 g.
Pick the answers to the questions out of the spilt popcorn.

a 10% of the bucket weighs _____
b 60% of the bucket weighs _____
c 5% of the bucket weighs _____
d 65% of the bucket weighs _____
e $2\frac{1}{2}$% of the bucket weighs _____
f $67\frac{1}{2}$% of the bucket weighs _____
g 85% of the bucket weighs _____

600g $2\frac{1}{2}$g 18g 32g 8g 432g 16g 384g 6g 46g 544g 64g 416g 526g

5 A laptop computer usually has 60 GB of memory.
The computer shop is offering a new laptop with 15% extra memory.

a What is 15% of 60 GB?
b What size is the memory of the new laptop?

6 Two tubes of toothpaste are on 'Special Offer' at a supermarket.
'Sparkling Gnashers' toothpaste usually weighs 120g.
It now has an extra 20% free.
'Sizzling Smiles' toothpaste usually weighs 140g.
It now has an extra 10% free.

a Which special offer gives the most toothpaste?
b If the two tubes of toothpaste are the same price, which toothpaste is offering the best deal?

7 Write
a 25 g as a percentage of 1 kg
b 30p as a percentage of £15
c 5 ml as a percentage of 1 litre
d 5 mm as a percentage of 10 cm.

4a 4a 4a 5c 5c 5a

12.4 Proportion

1 Without a calculator, work out

a 1×1 b 2×2 c 3×3 d 4×4 e 5×5

f 6×6 g 7×7 h 8×8 i 9×9 j 10×10

k Look at your answers. What is the special name for these numbers?

2 Three in every five beads in this necklace are blue.
This means that $\frac{3}{5}$ of the beads are blue.
Make a necklace pattern where

a 3 in every 6 beads are blue

b 3 in every 7 beads are blue

c 3 in every 4 beads are blue.

3 What proportion of the beads in each of these necklaces are yellow?
Give your answers as fractions.

a   b   c

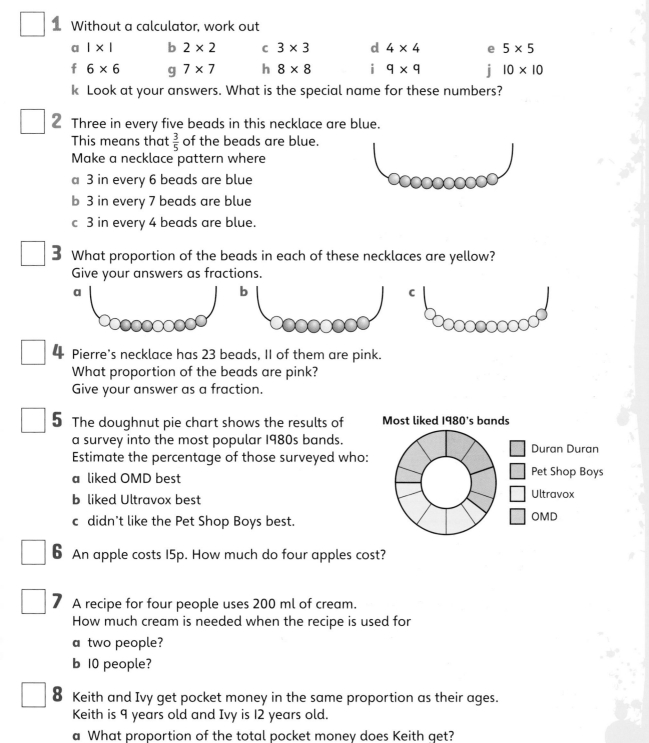

4 Pierre's necklace has 23 beads, 11 of them are pink.
What proportion of the beads are pink?
Give your answer as a fraction.

5 The doughnut pie chart shows the results of
a survey into the most popular 1980s bands.
Estimate the percentage of those surveyed who:

a liked OMD best

b liked Ultravox best

c didn't like the Pet Shop Boys best.

Most liked 1980's bands

- Duran Duran
- Pet Shop Boys
- Ultravox
- OMD

6 An apple costs 15p. How much do four apples cost?

7 A recipe for four people uses 200 ml of cream.
How much cream is needed when the recipe is used for

a two people?

b 10 people?

8 Keith and Ivy get pocket money in the same proportion as their ages.
Keith is 9 years old and Ivy is 12 years old.

a What proportion of the total pocket money does Keith get?

b Keith and Ivy get £14 pocket money between them.
How much do they each get?

12.5 Ratio

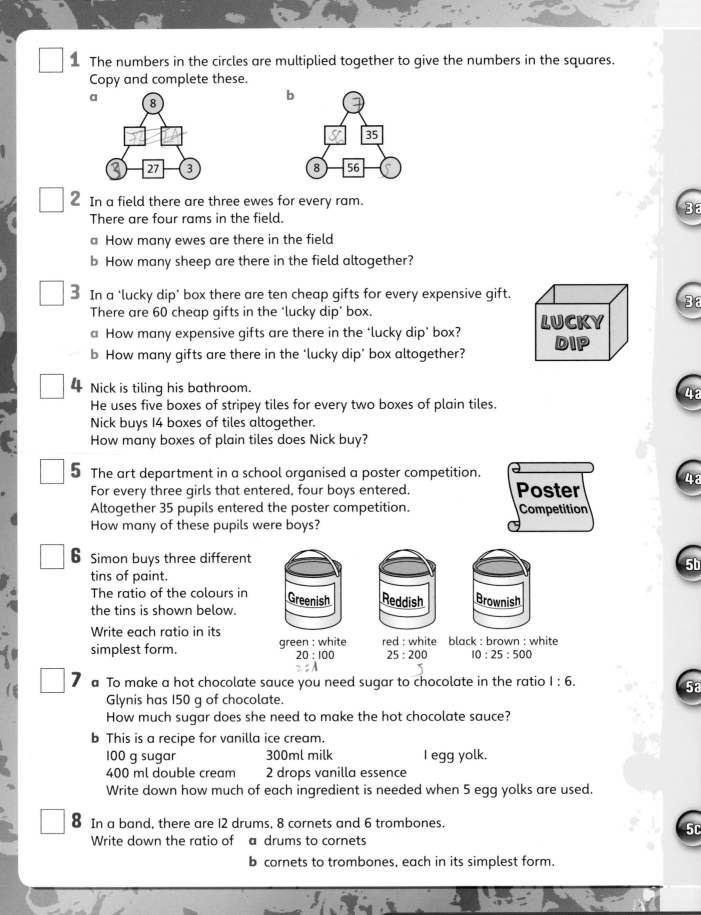

1 The numbers in the circles are multiplied together to give the numbers in the squares.
Copy and complete these.

a
  8
  27   3

b
  7
  35
  8   56

2 In a field there are three ewes for every ram.
There are four rams in the field.

a How many ewes are there in the field

b How many sheep are there in the field altogether?

3 In a 'lucky dip' box there are ten cheap gifts for every expensive gift.
There are 60 cheap gifts in the 'lucky dip' box.

a How many expensive gifts are there in the 'lucky dip' box?

b How many gifts are there in the 'lucky dip' box altogether?

LUCKY DIP

4 Nick is tiling his bathroom.
He uses five boxes of stripey tiles for every two boxes of plain tiles.
Nick buys 14 boxes of tiles altogether.
How many boxes of plain tiles does Nick buy?

5 The art department in a school organised a poster competition.
For every three girls that entered, four boys entered.
Altogether 35 pupils entered the poster competition.
How many of these pupils were boys?

Poster Competition

6 Simon buys three different tins of paint.
The ratio of the colours in the tins is shown below.

Write each ratio in its simplest form.

Greenish   Reddish   Brownish

green : white   red : white   black : brown : white
20 : 100   25 : 200   10 : 25 : 500

7 a To make a hot chocolate sauce you need sugar to chocolate in the ratio 1 : 6.
Glynis has 150 g of chocolate.
How much sugar does she need to make the hot chocolate sauce?

b This is a recipe for vanilla ice cream.
100 g sugar   300ml milk   1 egg yolk.
400 ml double cream   2 drops vanilla essence
Write down how much of each ingredient is needed when 5 egg yolks are used.

8 In a band, there are 12 drums, 8 cornets and 6 trombones.
Write down the ratio of   a drums to cornets

b cornets to trombones, each in its simplest form.

3a
3a
4a
4a
5b
5a
5c

13.1 Brackets blast-off!

1 The numbers in the two circles add together to give the number in the square between them.
Copy and complete the diagram.

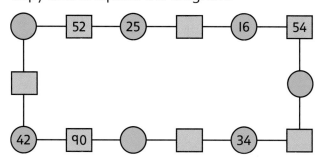

2 Write down whether A or B is the correct answer for each of these.

a $4 + 3 \times 2 =$ **A** 14   **B** 10

b $2 \times (9 - 5) =$ **A** 8   **B** 13

c $8 + 6 \div 2 =$ **A** 11   **B** 7

d $(9 + 12) \div 3 =$ **A** 7   **B** 13

e $20 \div 4 + 6 =$ **A** 2   **B** 11

3 Copy this table.

	question	working	answer
a	$3 \times (16 - 7)$	$16 \div 4$	3
b	$16 \div (7 - 3)$	$48 - 7$	37
c	$(16 - 7) \div 3$	3×9	4
d	$3 \times 16 - 7$	$16 + 21$	41
e	$16 + 3 \times 7$	$9 \div 3$	27

Draw a line linking the question on the left, to the working in the middle, to the answer on the right.
The first one is done for you.

4 Work out the answers to these.

a $(3 + 2)^2$ **b** $3 + 2^2$ **c** $6^2 - (4 + 9)$ **d** $6^2 - 4 + 9$

e $(11 - 3)^2 + 16$ **f** $11 - 3^2 + 16$ **g** $100 - (12 - 5)^2$ **h** $100 - 12 - 5^2$

5 a The answers to these questions are in the cloud.
Multiply out:

    i $4 \times (6 + x)$ **ii** $3(8 + x)$

   iii $6 \times (x - 3)$ **iv** $2(x - 9)$

    v $10 \times (2x + 4)$ **vi** $5(4x - 8)$

         $20x - 40$ $2x - 18$

             $24 + 4x$

    $6x - 18$ $20x + 40$

           $24 + x$

b Which two answers from the $6x - 3$ $24 + 3x$
cloud have not been used?

13.2 More simplifying expressions

1 I am thinking of a negative number.
I add 6 then subtract 2.
My answer is −3.
What is the number I was thinking of?

2 Write these algebraic expressions as simply as possible.

a $3a + 4a - 5a$ **b** $3b + 6 + b - 3$

3 Write an expression for the perimeter of each hexagon.
Simplify the expression.

a **b** 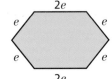 **c**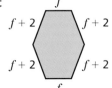

4 Write an expression for the perimeter of each quadrilateral.
Simplify the expression.

a **b** 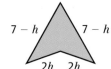 **c**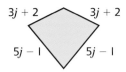

5 Simplify the following expressions.

a $3k + 2l + l + l$ **b** $5m - 2n - 3m$ **c** $2 + 3p + 7q + 5 + 3q$

6 Write an expression for the perimeter of each pentagon.
Collect any like terms.

a 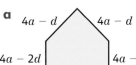 **b** 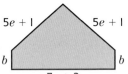 **c**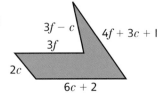

7 Simplify these algebraic expressions.

a $3 \times 5e$ **b** $3d \times 2$ **c** $8c \div 4$ **d** $100b \div 25$ **e** $0.5 \times 20a$

8 Multiply out these brackets.

a $5(x + 2)$ **b** $4(y - 5)$ **c** $3(6a + 7)$ **d** $2(7b - 2c + 4)$

13.3 Writing and solving one-step equations

1 Nico and his friend buy a pack of sandwiches for £1.96.
They share the cost equally between them.
How much do they each pay?
Give your answer in pence.

2 Angharad thinks of a mystery number.
She calls her number n.
Write an expression that is

  a 2 more than the number   **b** 2 less than the number

  c 3 times the number   **d** the number divided by 3

3 Copy this code grid.

7	2	10	7	4	6	5	1	8	10	9	3	11	12	1	13	3	11	14	2	10	11	15	9	13	13
								a															a		

Solve these equations to find the value of the letters in the code.
Complete the code grid. The first letter has been done for you.

  a $a + 2 = 11$ **b** $y + 5 = 10$ **c** $20 - i = 13$

  d $e - 9 = 2$ **e** $u - 3 = 5$ **f** $l + 7 = 20$

  g $d + 26 = 40$ **h** $100 - o = 99$ **i** $60 = 75 - m$

  j $36 = 24 + s$ **k** $7t = 14$ **l** $10v = 30$

  m $\dfrac{n}{2} = 2$ **n** $\dfrac{k}{1} = 6$ **o** $\dfrac{h}{2} = 5$

4 I think of a mystery number n.
I add 7 to it.

  a Write an expression for the new amount.

  b The answer after I have added 7 is 20.

  Write an equation involving n and solve it to find the value of n.

5 I think of a mystery number x.
I subtract 5 from it.

  a Write an expression for the new amount.

  b The answer after I have subtracted 5 is 20.

  Write an equation involving x and solve it to find the value of x.

6 I think of a mystery number a.
I multiply it by 10.

  a Write an expression for the new amount.

  b The answer after I have multiplied by 10 is 45.

  Write an equation involving a and solve it to find the value of a.

13.4 Solving and checking two-step equations

1 Add these fractions.
Give your answers as a mixed number.

   a $\frac{5}{7} + \frac{5}{7}$ **b** $\frac{3}{4} + \frac{3}{4} + \frac{3}{4}$ **c** $\frac{2}{5} + \frac{4}{5} + \frac{2}{5}$

2 Lola thinks of a mystery number n.
Write an expression that is

   a four times the number

   b four times the number and then add 3

   c four times the number less 3

   d four times the number with 3 added and 3 subtracted

3 Solve the equations to find the value of the symbols.

   a $2♥ + 1 = 7$ **b** $3♠ + 6 = 21$ **c** $5♣ - 2 = 18$

4 Solve the equations to find the mystery numbers.

   a $50a - 20 = 80$ **b** $20 + 5b = 40$ **c** $8c + 1 = 25$

5 Solve the equations to find the mystery numbers.

   a $28 - 4d = 4$ **b** $15 - 3e = 3$ **c** $10f + 2 = 20$

6 Solve the equations to find the mystery numbers.

   a $\frac{g}{2} + 5 = 12$ **b** $\frac{h}{3} - 2 = 3$ **c** $\frac{j}{10} + 4 = 1$

7 Dafydd solves the equation $3x + 3 = 24$
His answer is 9.
By putting his answer into the equation, check if he is correct.

8 There are five counters in a bowl.
Greta empties four bags of counters into the bowl.

   a Using s to represent the number of counters in
a bag, write an expression to show the number
of counters in the bowl.

   b The total number of counters in the bowl is 73.
Write an equation and solve it to find the
value of s.

Play any game on the LiveText CD

14.1 Forming shapes with triangles

1 Copy these sequences and find the next three terms.

   a 50, 44, 38, 32, ...   b 46, 41, 36, 31, ...

   c 18, 8, −2, −12, ...   d 3.4, 3.1, 2.8, 2.5, ...

Refer to the tangram for Q2, Q3 and Q4.
A tangram is a type of puzzle.
A large square is cut up as shown.
You can use the pieces to make other shapes and pictures.
The pieces are not allowed to overlap.

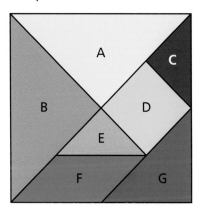

2 **Which two** pieces are a reflection of each other?

3 a Which **two** pieces can be joined to make a square?

   b Which **two** pieces can be joined to make a trapezium?

   c Which **three** pieces can be joined to make a rectangle that is not a square?

4 a Which **two** pieces are a rotation of each other?

   b Is it possible to make a kite from **two identical** pieces?

   c Is it possible to make a rhombus from **two identical** pieces?

   d Is it possible to make a rectangle from **two identical** pieces?

   e Are there any shapes with no lines of symmetry?

   f Are there any shapes with rotational symmetry of order 2?

Need some help? Look at Section 14.2 on the CD.

14.2 Translations

1 **a** Use any written method to calculate 346 × 27

Use your answer to part **a** to work out

b £3.46 × 27 **c** £34.60 × 27 **d** £2.70 × 346

2 Write down the correct description of the translation of A onto B.
Choose from the lists below.

a

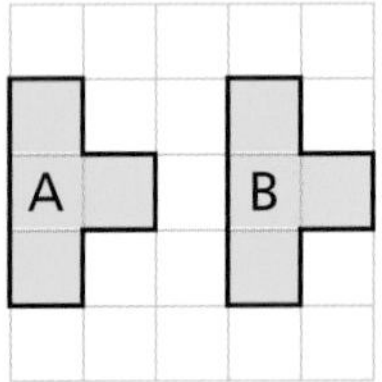

Slide A one square right.
Slide A two squares right.
Slide A three squares right.

b

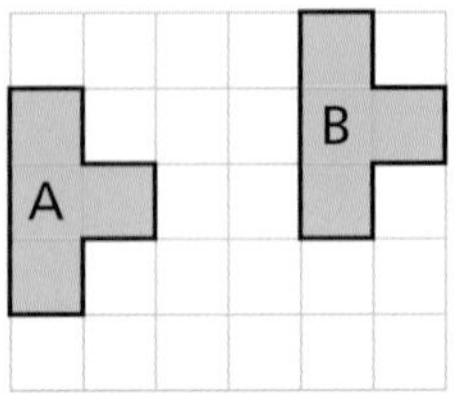

Slide A 2 squares right and 1 square up.
Slide A 3 squares left and 2 squares down.
Slide A 4 squares right and 1 square up.

3 Describe each translation of C onto D.

a

b

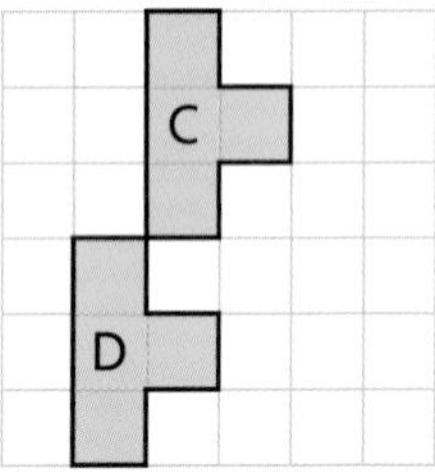

c

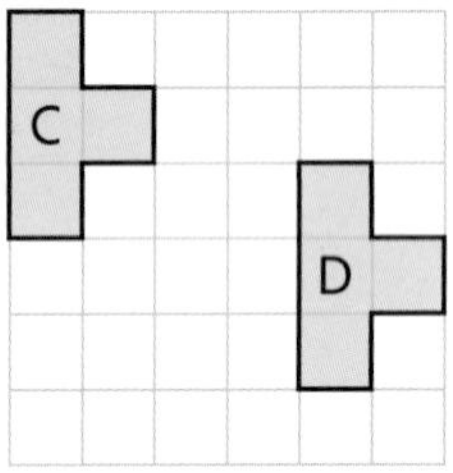

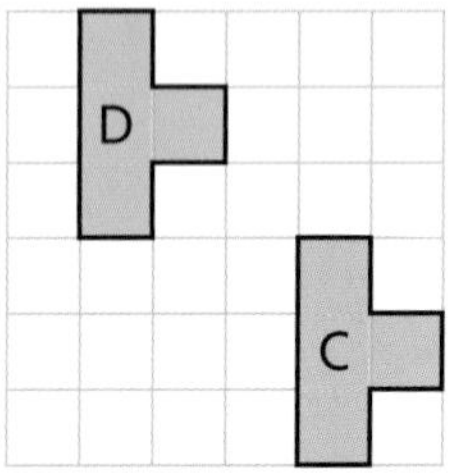

4 Gamba translates a point on a shape one right and four up.
The coordinates of the point before the translation were (1, 1).
What are the coordinates of the point after the translation?

5 Erin translates a triangle 2 left and 3 down.

a Copy and complete this table of coordinates.

b Name the type of triangle.

Point	Object	Image
A	(−2, 3)	
B	(2, 1)	
C		(−4, −2)

6 The point P (4, 1) is translated 2 right and 2 down to point Q.
The point Q is then translated 7 left and 2 down to point R.
Write down the coordinates of point R.

14.3 Reflecting shapes

1 Use your calculator to work out

   a 24^2 **b** $\sqrt{1764}$ **c** $15^2 - \sqrt{50176}$

2 Which drawings show a correct reflection of the pink shape in the dotted line?

  a 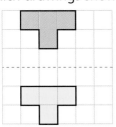   **b** 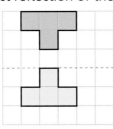   **c**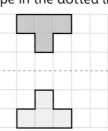

  d 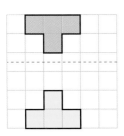   **e** 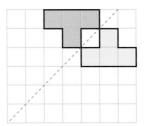   **f**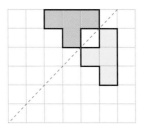

3 Copy each diagram and reflect the shape in the red mirror line.

  a 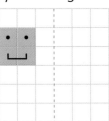   **b** 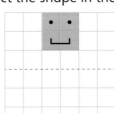   **c**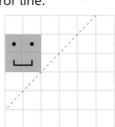

4 **a** Copy this diagram.
   b Reflect the shape in the line $x = -1$

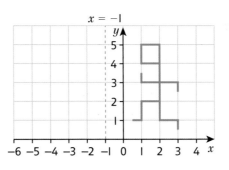

5 A triangle is reflected in the y-axis.
   Without drawing the triangle,
   copy and complete the table of coordinates.

Object	Image
$(-12, 6)$	
$(-4, 0)$	
$(-1, 1)$	

6 **a** Plot the points $(-2, 2)$, $(4, 2)$, $(3, 0)$, $(4, -2)$, $(-2, -2)$, $(-1, 0)$ and $(-2, 2)$.
      Join them in order to form a hexagon.
   b Which of these are lines of symmetry?
      The x-axis, the y-axis, $x = 1$, $y = 1$

14.4 Build a monster trap

1 Copy and complete:

    a 25 × 10 = _____   **b** 900 ÷ 100 = _____   **c** 4.3 × 100 = _____

    d 46 ÷ 10 = _____   **e** _____ ÷ 10 = 24   **f** 3.2 × _____ = 320

    g 0.55 × _____ = 5.5   **h** _____ ÷ 100 = 0.08

2 Use the words and numbers from the boxes to complete the descriptions on how to rotate shape A to shape B in each diagram.

(3,3) (6,3) (1,3)	clockwise anticlockwise	45° 90° 180°

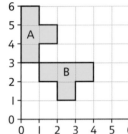 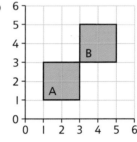 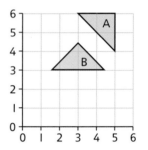

    a Rotate shape A _____ in a _____ direction about centre _____.

    b Rotate shape A _____ in a _____ direction about centre _____.

    c Rotate shape A _____ in a _____ direction about centre _____.

3 Copy these shapes.

    a Take one square from shape C and add it to shape D so that both shapes have rotational symmetry of order 2.

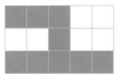 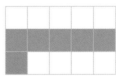

    b Take one square from shape E and add it to shape F so that both shapes have rotational symmetry of order 4.

    c Take two squares from shape G and add them to shape H so that both shapes have rotational symmetry of order 2.

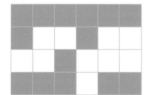 

14.5 Combining transformations

1 Use the column method to work out the answers to these.

  a 4036 + 294   **b** 76.4 + 18.3   **c** 275.81 + 9.6

2 The green trapezium can be reflected onto each of the coloured trapeziums.
Which trapezium is a reflection of the green trapezium in the line

  a AE?   **b** CG?   **c** BF?   **d** DH?

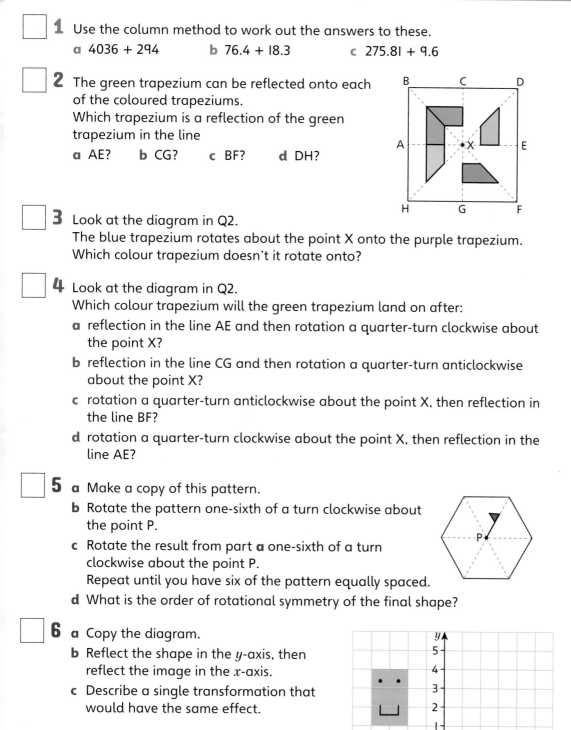

3 Look at the diagram in Q2.
The blue trapezium rotates about the point X onto the purple trapezium.
Which colour trapezium doesn't it rotate onto?

4 Look at the diagram in Q2.
Which colour trapezium will the green trapezium land on after:

  a reflection in the line AE and then rotation a quarter-turn clockwise about the point X?

  b reflection in the line CG and then rotation a quarter-turn anticlockwise about the point X?

  c rotation a quarter-turn anticlockwise about the point X, then reflection in the line BF?

  d rotation a quarter-turn clockwise about the point X, then reflection in the line AE?

5 **a** Make a copy of this pattern.

  b Rotate the pattern one-sixth of a turn clockwise about the point P.

  c Rotate the result from part **a** one-sixth of a turn clockwise about the point P.
  Repeat until you have six of the pattern equally spaced.

  d What is the order of rotational symmetry of the final shape?

6 **a** Copy the diagram.

  b Reflect the shape in the y-axis, then reflect the image in the x-axis.

  c Describe a single transformation that would have the same effect.

14.6 Problem solving

1 Emyr worked out 57.6 cm add 1.3 m on his calculator.
He got an answer of 58.9 This answer is wrong.
  a What mistake did Emyr make?
  b Write down the correct answer.

2 An equilateral triangle has a perimeter of 60 cm.
How long is each side?

3 A square has a perimeter of 60 cm.
How long is each side?

4 A regular pentagon has a perimeter of 60 cm.
How long is each side?

5 A regular hexagon has a perimeter of 60 cm.
How long is each side?

6 **a** Make two copies of the grid onto centimetre
squared paper.
  b Complete one copy to make a rectangle with
a perimeter of 12 cm.
  c Complete the other copy to make a rectangle
with an area of 12 cm².

7 The area of the shaded triangle is 100 cm².
  a Find the length x.
  b Work out the perimeter of the rectangle.
  c Ryan says that the perimeter of a rectangle
is always an even number.
Give a counter example to show that this is
not true.

x cm

←10 cm→

8 This sequence is made from identical equilateral triangles.
Each triangle has sides of length 6 cm.
Here are the first three shapes in the sequence.
  a Work out the perimeter of the first three shapes in the sequence.
  b Work out the perimeter of the 20th shape in the sequence.
  c One of the shapes has a perimeter of 48 cm.
Which position is this in the sequence?

9 The surface area of this cube is 150 cm².
Find the length x cm.

x cm

Play any game on the LiveText CD

15.1 Probability and outcomes

1 Change each improper fraction to a mixed number.

a $\frac{7}{2}$ b $\frac{15}{9}$ c $\frac{27}{4}$ d $\frac{98}{10}$

2 Draw a probability scale from 0 to I.
Mark each of the probabilities on it.

a I will flip a coin and get 'tails'.

b A cat will live to be 270 years old.

c The sun will rise tomorrow.

3 Copy and complete this probability scale using the words:

sometimes   always   no way! $\frac{1}{2}$ the time   usually

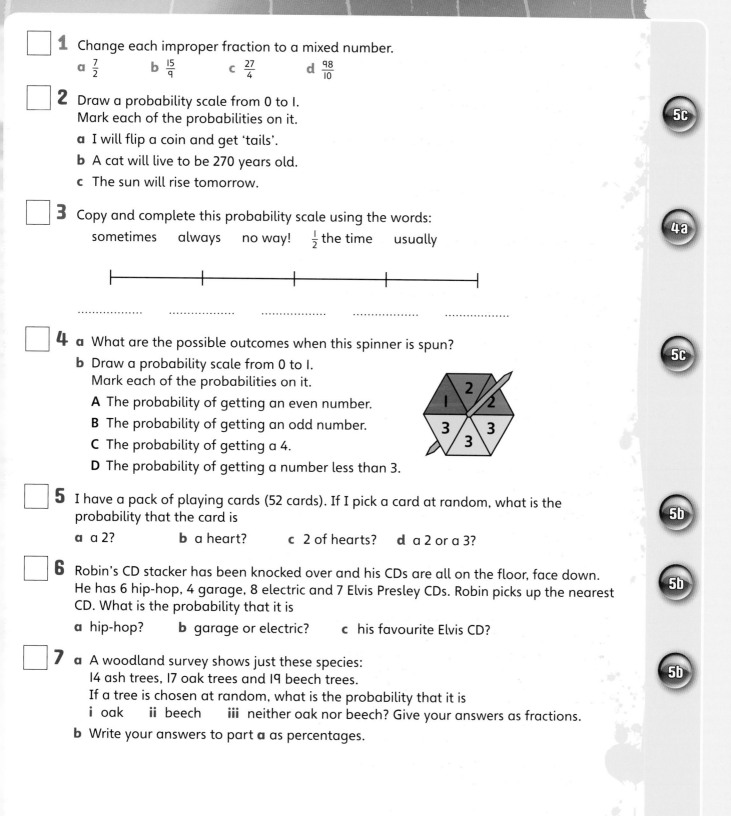

....

4 a What are the possible outcomes when this spinner is spun?

b Draw a probability scale from 0 to I.
Mark each of the probabilities on it.

A The probability of getting an even number.

B The probability of getting an odd number.

C The probability of getting a 4.

D The probability of getting a number less than 3.

5 I have a pack of playing cards (52 cards). If I pick a card at random, what is the probability that the card is

a a 2?   b a heart?   c 2 of hearts?   d a 2 or a 3?

6 Robin's CD stacker has been knocked over and his CDs are all on the floor, face down.
He has 6 hip-hop, 4 garage, 8 electric and 7 Elvis Presley CDs. Robin picks up the nearest
CD. What is the probability that it is

a hip-hop?   b garage or electric?   c his favourite Elvis CD?

7 a A woodland survey shows just these species:
14 ash trees, 17 oak trees and 19 beech trees.
If a tree is chosen at random, what is the probability that it is
i oak   ii beech   iii neither oak nor beech? Give your answers as fractions.

b Write your answers to part **a** as percentages.

15.2 Sample space diagrams

1 By working out 10% then 5%, find 15% of
    a £600   **b** 700 g   **c** 2 kg   **Hint** Change 2 kg into grams.

2 A normal £1 coin is flipped.
    a What is the probability of it landing on 'heads'?
    b What is the probability of it landing on 'tails'?
    c What do you notice about your answers to parts **a** and **b**? Explain.

3 A normal pack of 52 cards is shuffled and a card is chosen at random.
    a What is the probability of the card being a heart?
    b What is the probability of the card not being a heart?

4 The probability of Steve missing his flight is 0.005.
    What is the probability of Steve not missing his flight?

5 The probability of Steve getting turbulence on his flight is $\frac{1}{75}$.
    What is the probability of Steve not getting turbulence on his flight?

6 A coin is flipped and a normal dice is rolled.
    a Use a sample space diagram to list all of the possible outcomes.
    b How many outcomes are there?

7 You can choose any two toppings for your ice cream from:
    flakes, nuts, sprinkles
    What are the possible combinations of toppings?

8 Nasir spins a coin three times.
    How many possible outcomes are there?

5b
5a
5a
5a
5a
5a
5a

15.3 Experimental probability

1 Work out
  a 3 × 7 + 2 **b** 3 + 2 × 3 **c** 6 + 8 × 2 − 1
  d 2 + (3 × 3) − 4 **e** 300 + (20 − 10)²

2 Mildred has 100 beads in a bag. The beads are silver, black and gold. Mildred does not know how many of each colour there are. She carries out an experiment to help her guess the right number of beads of each colour. She takes a bead from the bag, records its colour then replaces the bead. She does this 40 times. Her results are shown in this table.

Colour	Tally	Frequency	Estimated probability
Silver	ЖЖ ЖЖ ll		
Black	ЖЖ ЖЖ ЖЖ ЖЖ		
Gold	ЖЖ lll		

  a Copy and complete the table.
  b Use the estimated probability to calculate the number of silver, black and gold beads in the bag.

3 Mike thinks that a dice is not fair. He rolls the dice 100 times and records the results.

Outcome	Tally	Frequency	Estimated probability
1	ЖЖ ЖЖ ЖЖ ll		
2	ЖЖ ll		
3	ЖЖ ЖЖ ЖЖ ll		
4	ЖЖ ЖЖ ЖЖ ЖЖ ЖЖ		
5	ЖЖ ЖЖ llll		
6	ЖЖ ЖЖ ЖЖ ЖЖ		

  a Copy and complete the table.
  b Use the estimated probability to decide if Mike's dice is fair or not. Explain your answer.

4 Ave flipped a coin 50 times and recorded 28 'heads'.
Blaine flipped a coin 50 times and recorded 23 'heads'.
  a What was Ave's estimated probability of getting a 'head'?
  b What was Blaine's estimated probability of getting a 'head'?
  c What was their combined estimated probability of getting a 'head'?
  d Which answer, **a**, **b** or **c**, is the closest to the theoretical probability of getting a 'head'?

15.4 More on displaying data

1 Petrol costs 115.9p per litre.
Caroline fills her petrol tank with 38.62 litres.
How much does she pay for this petrol?

2 These are the sales figures for a 10 minute period on Monday lunchtime at Sam's Sandwich Bar.

a Draw a bar chart to display the data.

b How many sandwiches were sold altogether in the 10 minute period?

Filling	Frequency
BLT	8
Cheese and marmite	4
Tikka	12
Egg mayo	7

3 These are the sales figures for a 10 minute period on Saturday lunchtime at Sam's Sandwich Bar.

a Draw a bar line graph to display the data.

b How many sandwiches were sold altogether in the 10 minute period?

Filling	Frequency
BLT	21
Cheese and marmite	14
Tikka	30
Egg mayo	8

4 The number of sandwiches sold in 10 minute periods at Sam's Sandwich Bar on Saturday is shown in the table.

a Draw a bar chart to display the data.

b How many 10 minute periods were there on the Saturday?

Sandwiches sold	Frequency
0 - 19	3
20 - 39	12
40 - 59	13
60 - 79	11
80 - 99	8
100 - 119	1

5 30 train passengers were asked to give a mark out of 100 for the quality of the food in the buffet carriage.

```
10   25   50   35   10   15   45   55   50   30
30   15   25   25   50   35   40    5   20   35
45   50   40   30   30   25   35   47   25   10
```

Using class intervals 0–9, 10–19, 20–29 and so on, construct a frequency table for the data.

6 Some passengers on a train were asked to give a mark out of 50 for the politeness of the staff.

```
30   40   35   25   40   45   30   32   30
15   25   40   30   25   10
```

a Decide on suitable class intervals and construct a frequency table for the data.

b How many train passengers took part in this survey?

7 During one month, an agent sold the phones as shown in the table.
Construct and label a pie chart to show this information.

Phone	Number sold
y-phone	170
Samey 300	200
Bensung	125
Mokia 6L	105

15.5 Interpreting charts and graphs

1 Dave buys a 750 m reel of fishing line for £6.99

   a How many metres does Dave get for each £1 spent?

   b What is the cost per metre of the fishing line?

2

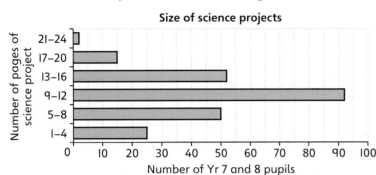

Size of science projects

   a How many pupil's science projects were between 13 and 16 pages?

   b How many pupils took part in this survey?

3 The frequency table shows the number of pages in the year 9, 10 and 11 pupil's science projects.

   a How many pupils wrote 11–15 pages?

   b How many pupils wrote more than 20 pages?

   c How many pupils wrote a science project in years 9, 10 and 11?

Number of pages	Frequency
1–5	27
6–10	50
11–15	66
16–20	117
21–25	63
26–30	7

4

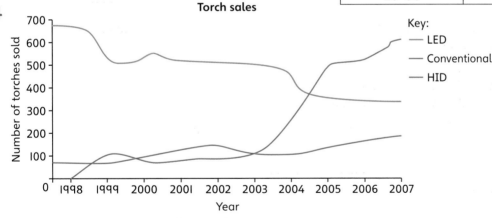

Torch sales

Key:
— LED
— Conventional
— HID

   a When were LED torches first sold?

   b Describe what is happening to conventional bulb torch sales from 1998 to 2007.

5 The pie chart represents light bulb sales in Spain 2006.

   a Which type of bulb has had the least sales?

   b Approximately what fraction of the light bulb sales were conventional bulbs?

   c The total sales in 2006 were 32.6 million. Estimate the number of conventional bulbs sold.

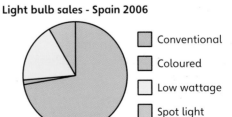

Light bulb sales - Spain 2006

Conventional
Coloured
Low wattage
Spot light

15.6 Statistics

1 The answer to a calculation is 3275.0944
  a If this answer is in pounds, round to give a sensible answer.
  b If this answer is in pence, round to give a sensible answer.
  c Round the answer to the nearest 100.

You will need this table of the South Pembrokeshire short-mat bowls league to answer Q2 to 6.

	Played	Won	Drew	Lost	Shots For	Shots Against	Points
Little Haven	20	11	2	7	813	515	102
Freystrop	20	11	2	7	717	559	97
Hook	20	9	6	5	679	559	96
Penally	20	13	3	4	753	528	95
Tavernspite	20	10	5	5	673	594	95
The Badgers	20	9	4	7	664	579	91
Tabernacle	20	9	2	9	615	688	77
Letterston	20	3	8	9	595	683	74

2 What is the mode of
  a the number of games played?
  b the number of games lost?

3 What is the range of
  a the number of points scored?
  b the number of shots against?

4 What is the median number of
  a games lost?
  b games won?

5 Calculate the mean number of points scored.

6 Greg and Brendan scored these points in their last 8 short-mat bowls matches:
Greg   8, 6, 6, 12, 7, 10, 6, 11
Brendan 5, 15, 21, 3, 11, 18, 1, 4
  a Calculate the mean and range for each set of data.
  b Who is the better bowler? Give reasons for your answer.

7 a Copy and complete the table.
  b Calculate the mean number of games played.

Number of games played	Frequency	No. games × freq.
1	4	
2	6	
3	8	
4	2	

4b
4b
4a
5c
5c
5b

15.7 Collecting the right data

1 Estimate the answer to these.

    a 39×52 **b** 298×6 **c** 611×7.82

2 Sam's Sandwich Bar would like to know about customers' favourite filling. Which data would be relevant?

    A How many people came in each group   **B** Are they vegetarian or not?

    C Do they buy sandwiches often?   **D** Which day(s) they buy sandwiches

    E Age of customer   **F** Weight of customer

    G Number of sandwiches bought

(4a)

3 Sam's Sandwich Bar wants to introduce a luxury and a deluxe range of baguettes.
The luxury range will be sweet chilli and red pepper or chorizo.
The deluxe range will be prawn cocktail or peppered steak.
Design a data collection sheet to find out what price customers would pay.

(4a)

4 What data would be needed to investigate at what time of day customers visit Sam's Sandwich Bar?

(5c)

5 How should Sam obtain data for Q4?

(5c)

6 Sam wants to find out what customers think of the politeness of his staff. Sam's Sandwich Bar serves about 400 people most weekdays. He is thinking of asking every customer on a weekday.

    a What are the advantages and disadvantages of asking all 400 people?

    b What sample size might be better?

(5c)

7 Are these questions suitable for Sam's questionnaire in Q6? If not, give a reason and rewrite the question to make it more sensible.

    a Age   0-1 ☐   2-3 ☐   4-5 ☐   6-70 ☐

    b Most of our customers really like our tikka sandwiches, do you?

        Yes ☐   Not sure ☐

    c Apart from our healthy range of sandwiches, what is your favourite health food?

        Salad ☐   Cereal bars ☐   Other ☐

(5a)

15.8 Statistical enquiry

1 **a** Give the first four multiples of five.

   b Find at least four factors of 36.

2 Mahmoud complains that Tayser's dice is unfair. He thinks it lands on 6 too often. To investigate, they each roll the dice 18 times.

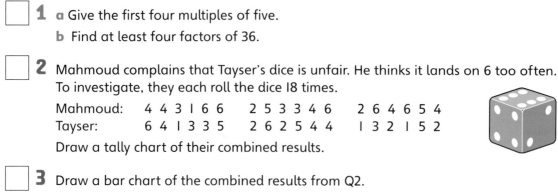

Mahmoud: 4 4 3 1 6 6   2 5 3 3 4 6   2 6 4 6 5 4
Tayser: 6 4 1 3 3 5   2 6 2 5 4 4   1 3 2 1 5 2

Draw a tally chart of their combined results.

3 Draw a bar chart of the combined results from Q2.

4 **a** What is the modal number of the combined results in Q2?

   b Do you think Mahmoud is correct? Is the dice unfair?

Mahmoud and Tayser have been playing cards on their holiday.
They have kept a record of how many games each has won over the week.

	Sat	Sun	Mon	Tue	Wed	Thur	Fri
Mahmoud:	17	12	16	16	16	13	15
Tayser:	28	18	14	12	16	21	10

5 What is the range of each set of data?

6 What is the mean of each set of data?

7 Use the range and mean to explain who is best at cards, Mahmoud or Tayser.

4c

4c

4b

4b

5c

5b

16.1 More addition and subtraction

1 Add together mentally.

a 5 + 5 + 8   b 7 + 3 + 6   c 8 + 4 + 2   d 9 + 6 + 4

2 In the number pyramids, the value in each brick is the sum of the values in the two bricks below.
Copy and complete the pyramids.

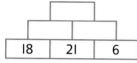 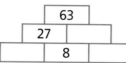 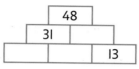

18	21	6

63
27	
8	

48
31	
	13

3 Copy and complete:

a 54 + ☐ = 100   b ☐ + 17 = 100

c 100 = ☐ + 79   d 37p + ☐ = £1.00

4 The red cards are question cards.
The blue cards are answer cards.
Match each red card with the correct blue card.

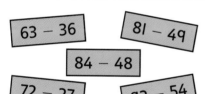
63 − 36   81 − 49   84 − 48   72 − 27   92 − 54

32   27   36   38   45

5 Use the column method to do these calculations.

a 417 + 232   b 744 + 57   c 846 − 333   d 806 − 567

6 Zaid worked out 784 + 423 and got an answer of 1207.
Use approximation to work out if Zaid is correct.

7 Use the column method to do these calculations.

a 12.4 + 21.3   b 272.6 + 21.5   c 275.5 g + 12.25 g
d 6.85 − 1.25   e 272.6 − 26.9   f 385.5 g − 28.65 g

16.2 More multiples and factors

1 Work out the answers to these.

a $\frac{3}{7} - \frac{1}{7}$

b $\frac{13}{17} - \frac{11}{17}$

c $\frac{7}{8} - \frac{2}{8}$

d $\frac{10}{11} - \frac{9}{11}$

2 The number 72 has 12 factors.
Copy and complete this factor diagram.
Some of the factors have been found for you.
Find as many of the other factors as you can.

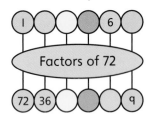

3 Write down the numbers from the cloud that are

a multiples of 4

b multiples of 5.

4 Ana says that her favourite number is 36 because

a it is a multiple of 2

b it is a multiple of 3

c it is a multiple of 4

d it is a multiple of 5

e it is a multiple of 6

f it is a multiple of 7

g 9 is a factor of 36

h 10 is a factor of 36

i 12 is a factor of 36

j 18 is a factor of 36

k 72 is a factor of 36

l 72 is a multiple of 36

Ana has made some mistakes.
Which of her statements are **not** true?

5 Find the common factors of 4 and 14.

6 Find the highest common factor (HCF) of these numbers.

a 14 and 21

b 12, 15 and 27

7 Find the lowest common multiple (LCM) of these numbers.

a 5 and 9

b 3, 4 and 10

16.3 Factors, multiples and primes

1 Calculate

    a $4 \times 3 + 5$ **b** $5 + 3 \times 4$ **c** $10 \times 0.5 - 2$ **d** $10 - 0.5 \times 2$

2 Write down the numbers from the cloud that are

    a divisible by 2   **b** divisible by 5

    c divisible by 2 and 5   **d** divisible by 10.

Numbers in cloud: 2, 3, 4, 5, 7, 8, 20, 9, 6, 10, 18, 30, 23, 48, 25, 50

 4c

3 Sian has a bag of 35 marbles.

    Can these be shared equally between

    a 10 friends?   **b** 2 friends?   **c** 5 friends?

 4c

4 Write down three numbers that are divisible by 2, 5 and 10.

 4c

5 Copy and complete the following table.

Write ✓ or ✗ to show whether each number is divisible by 3, 4, 6 and 9.
Two entries have been done for you.

Number	Divisible by 3	Divisible by 4	Divisible by 6	Divisible by 9
36	✓			
45			✗	
48				
123				
261				

 4c

6 Write down three numbers that are divisible by 2 and 25.

 4c

7 Which of these numbers are prime numbers?

    3   13   23   33   43   53   63   73   83   93

 4a

8 Copy this number grid.

You must work your way across the grid by
shading one square at a time.
You can only go up or down or to the right.
You can only shade prime numbers.
You must start on square S, and finish on square F.
The first two moves have been shaded for you.

S	2	39	15	33	14	30
4	5	18	22	6	50	45
9	11	23	17	40	27	12
22	51	20	29	31	8	48
46	60	55	1	7	3	52
25	24	66	16	21	19	26
66	35	28	42	10	37	F

 4a

9 **a** Write down the factors of 54.

    b Write down the prime factors of 54.

 4a

10 Write down the LCM of

    a 12 and 18   **b** 20 and 25

 5c

16.4 More multiplication

1 Write these cards in order of size, starting with the smallest.

$\frac{1}{2}$ of £28.50	$\frac{1}{3}$ of £39	$\frac{1}{4}$ of £56

2 Brian buys five pencils costing 34p each.
How much does he pay in total?

3 Caitlin pays her accountant £275 an hour.
How much does Caitlin pay her accountant for three hours work?

4 John went to a horse sale and bought six horses.
The horses cost £1850 each.
How much did John pay for the six horses?

5 Enrique buys 25 tins of paint for £12 each.
How much does Enrique pay in total?

6 Fergal buys 18 tins of beans.
Each tin weighs 225 g.
What is the total weight of the beans?

7 Gustaw buys four jars of luxury jam.
Each jar of jam costs £2.95
How much does Gustaw pay altogether?

8 Use the $\boxed{x^2}$ or $\boxed{\sqrt{}}$ keys on your calculator to find the missing numbers.

  a $27 \times 27 = \boxed{}$ **b** $35^2 = \boxed{}$ **c** $\boxed{}^2 = 324$

9 This is a CCC (Calculation Challenge Curve). Copy the curve.
Start at the first calculation and use your calculator to fill in the missing values.

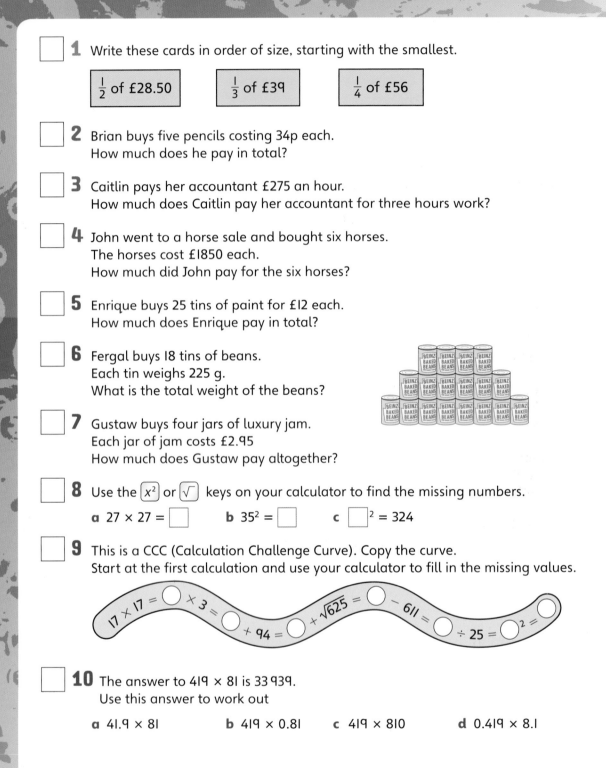

$17 \times 17 = \bigcirc \times 3 = \bigcirc + 94 = \bigcirc + \sqrt{625} = \bigcirc - 611 = \bigcirc \div 25 = \bigcirc^2 = \bigcirc$

10 The answer to 419×81 is $33\,939$.
Use this answer to work out

  a 41.9×81 **b** 419×0.81 **c** 419×810 **d** 0.419×8.1

16.5 More division

1 I think of a number.
I add 2 to the number, then I subtract 10.
My answer is −3.
What was the number I thought of?

2 One tray has 256 chocolates on it.
One box contains 12 chocolates.
Use your calculator to work out how many
boxes can be filled from one tray of chocolates.

3 One tin of paint covers 11 square metres of wall.
Jane wants to paint 72 square metres.
How many tins of paint must she buy?

4 Liam fills his fishpond with water.
He uses a bucket that holds 6 litres.
His fishpond holds 350 litres of water.
Use your calculator to work out how many times
Liam has to fill his bucket to completely fill his pond.

5 Chris pays £28 each month for pet insurance.
Chris has four dogs.
How much does Chris pay per month for each dog?

6 Seven people share the cost of hiring a hall for a party.
The hall costs £245.
Use a written method to work out how much each person pays.

7 Diego earned £996 in his 12 week summer holiday.
Use a written method to work out how much Diego earned each week.

8 Sally paid £2590 for a 14 day horse riding
holiday in America.
Use a written method to work out
how much the holiday cost per day.

9 Donna earned £584.50 in her 7 week summer holiday.
Use a written method to work out how much Donna earned each week.

3a

3a

3a

4a

4b

5b

5b

5a

16.6 Equivalent fractions, decimals and percentages

1 The red cards are question cards.
The blue cards are answer cards.
Match each red card with the correct blue card.

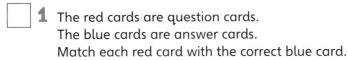

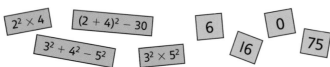

2 Are these true or false? Explain your answers.

a 52 out of 100 people prefer tea to coffee. That's about half.

b 38% of people surveyed prefer honey to jam. Of 200 people surveyed, 19 preferred honey.

3 Look at the following pizzas.

1   2   3

Amount eaten:	Pizza 1	Pizza 2	Pizza 3
Fraction			
Percentage			
Decimal			

Copy and complete this table to show how much of each pizza has been eaten.

4 Copy and complete this table.

Fraction	Percentage	Decimal
$\frac{3}{10}$		
$\frac{27}{100}$		
	40%	
	11%	
		0.85
		0.05

5 Copy and complete these equivalent fractions.

a $\times 5$
$$\frac{3}{4} = \frac{\square}{20}$$
$\times 5$

b $\div 5$
$$\frac{45}{100} = \frac{9}{\square}$$
$\div 5$

c $\times 4$
$$\frac{3}{25} = \frac{\square}{\square}$$
$\times 4$

6 Write each of these fractions in its simplest form.

a $\frac{8}{12}$ **b** $\frac{8}{18}$ **c** $\frac{18}{27}$ **d** $\frac{18}{21}$

7 a Use equivalent fractions to convert $\frac{7}{20}$ to a decimal.

b What is $\frac{7}{20}$ as a percentage?

16.7 Fractions cup final at Wembley

1 In this Wembley arch, numbers in the white circles next to each other add up to 100. Copy the arch and fill in the missing numbers.

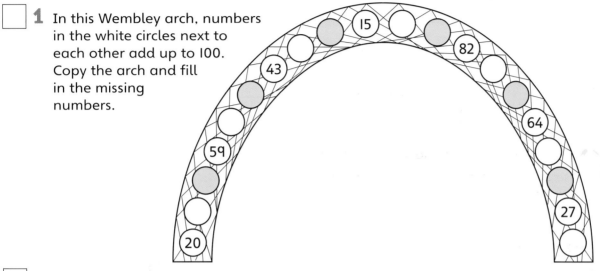

2 Work out

   a half of 24   **b** one third of 24   **c** one quarter of 60   **d** one fifth of 25

3 Work out

   a $\frac{1}{6}$ of £30   **b** $\frac{2}{3}$ of 12 kg   **c** $\frac{3}{4}$ of 20 litres   **d** $\frac{4}{5}$ of $35

4 David and Paul buy a Wembley season ticket between them. The ticket costs £2400. David pays $\frac{1}{3}$ of the cost of the ticket.

   a How much does David pay?   **b** How much does Paul pay?

5 Christos takes £40 spending money to Wembley. He spends $\frac{1}{4}$ of his money on a 'Wembley T-shirt'. How much does the 'Wembley T-shirt' cost?

6 Essien takes £30 spending money to Wembley. He spends $\frac{2}{5}$ of his money on a 'Wembley turf key ring'. How much does the 'Wembley turf key ring' cost?

7 Margot takes £40 spending money to Wembley. She spends $\frac{3}{20}$ of her money on a 'Wembley teddy bear'. How much does the 'Wembley teddy bear' cost?

8 Arrange these cards into groups that give the same answer.

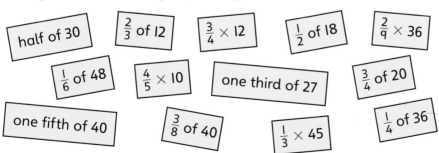

16.8 Calculations with percentages

1 Simplify these fractions by cancelling.

   a $\dfrac{6}{15} = \dfrac{\square}{5}$ b $\dfrac{7}{21} = \dfrac{\square}{3}$ c $\dfrac{10}{24} = \dfrac{5}{\square}$

2 Work out these in your head.

   a 10% of 370 kg   b 50% of £3.70   c 5% of £3700

3 Without a calculator, find 21% of each of these.

   a £220   b £180   c 7 kg

4 a Half of 10% is 5%. What is half of 5%?

   b Use the facts in part **a** to work out the following.
      i 10% of £500
      ii 5% of £500
      iii 2.5% of £500
      iv 17.5% of £500

   c Find 17.5% of £600, without a calculator.

5 Three scientists, Greg, John and Bron, study a coral reef.
They study 180 different types of live animal.
Greg says "15% are coral".
John says "3 out of every 10 are worms".
Bron says "35% are fish".

   Work out:

   a the number of coral

   b the number of worms

   c the number of fish

   d the number of animals that were **not** coral, worms or fish

   e the percentage of animals that were **not** coral, worms or fish.

6 Use your calculator to work out.

   a 17% of 140 kg   b 56% of £80   c 2% of 7 m   d 99.5% of £2

7 Use your calculator to work out.

   a 8% of 64   b 16% of 32   c 32% of 16   d 64% of 8

8 Write

   a 32 cm as a percentage of 1 m

   b £3 as a percentage of £25

   c 80 m as a percentage of 1 km.

17.1 Finding terms in a sequence

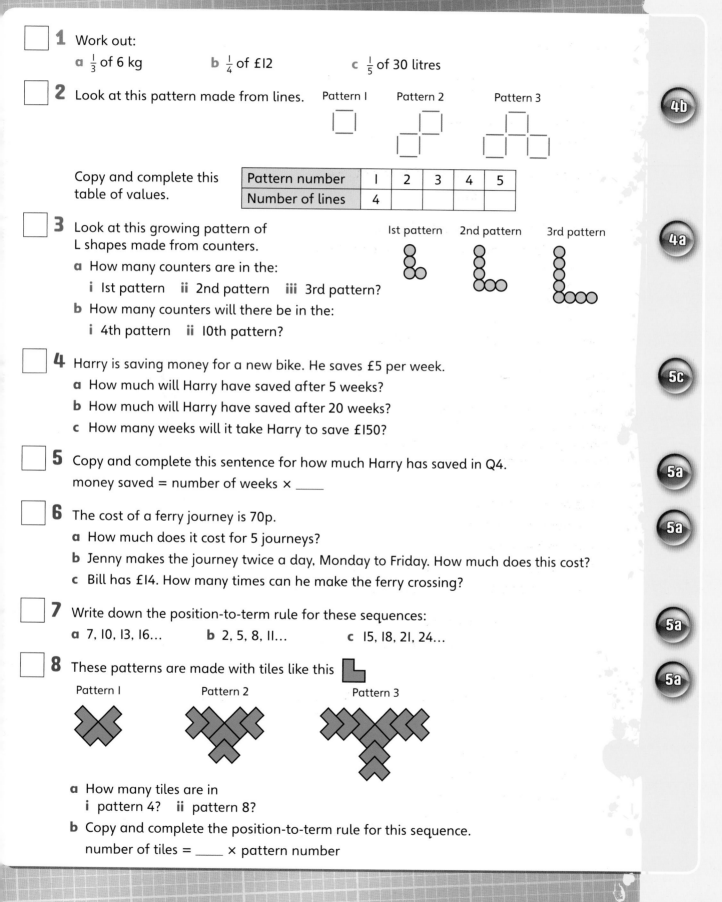

1 Work out:

    a $\frac{1}{3}$ of 6 kg   **b** $\frac{1}{4}$ of £12   **c** $\frac{1}{5}$ of 30 litres

2 Look at this pattern made from lines.

    Pattern 1   Pattern 2   Pattern 3

Copy and complete this table of values.

Pattern number	1	2	3	4	5
Number of lines	4				

3 Look at this growing pattern of L shapes made from counters.

    1st pattern   2nd pattern   3rd pattern

    a How many counters are in the:

        i 1st pattern   **ii** 2nd pattern   **iii** 3rd pattern?

    b How many counters will there be in the:

        i 4th pattern   **ii** 10th pattern?

4 Harry is saving money for a new bike. He saves £5 per week.

    a How much will Harry have saved after 5 weeks?

    b How much will Harry have saved after 20 weeks?

    c How many weeks will it take Harry to save £150?

5 Copy and complete this sentence for how much Harry has saved in Q4.

    money saved = number of weeks × _____

6 The cost of a ferry journey is 70p.

    a How much does it cost for 5 journeys?

    b Jenny makes the journey twice a day, Monday to Friday. How much does this cost?

    c Bill has £14. How many times can he make the ferry crossing?

7 Write down the position-to-term rule for these sequences:

    a 7, 10, 13, 16...   **b** 2, 5, 8, 11...   **c** 15, 18, 21, 24...

8 These patterns are made with tiles like this

    Pattern 1   Pattern 2   Pattern 3

    a How many tiles are in

        i pattern 4?   **ii** pattern 8?

    b Copy and complete the position-to-term rule for this sequence.

        number of tiles = _____ × pattern number

4b

4a

5c

5a

5a

5a

5a

17.2 More functions and mappings

1 | 1000 g = 1 kg | 1000 mg = 1 g |

Change the following masses into grams.
a 2 kg   b 7.3 kg   c 2500 mg   d 700 mg

2 This function machine can be used to generate multiples of 10.

$x \rightarrow \boxed{\times 10} \rightarrow y$

What will the y-value be if the x-value is
a 1?   b 7?   c 25?   d 3.5?

3 Find the outputs of these function machines.

a $x \rightarrow \boxed{+10} \rightarrow y$

x	1	2	4	8	16
y					

b $x \rightarrow \boxed{\times 5} \rightarrow y$

x	1	2	4	8	16
y					

c $x \rightarrow \boxed{\div 2} \rightarrow y$

x	1	2	4	8	16
y					

4 Match the function machine to the correct function.

$x \rightarrow \boxed{\times 8} \rightarrow y$

a $y = x + 8$
b $x = x + 8$
c $y = 8x$
d $y = \frac{8}{x}$
e $x = 8y$

5 This function machine can be used to generate odd numbers.

$x \rightarrow \boxed{\times 2 + 1} \rightarrow y$

Find the inputs for these outputs:
a 5   b 9   c 21   d 101

6 Find the missing parts of the rule in these functions.

a $x \rightarrow \boxed{} \rightarrow y$

11 → 20
2 → 11
6 → 15

b $x \rightarrow \boxed{\times 2} \rightarrow \boxed{} \rightarrow y$

11 → 20
2 → 2
6 → 10

7 Write down four different function machines that could map 5 → 20

17.3 More coordinates

1 Use any method to work out:

   a 23 × 31   **b** 48 × 25   **c** 13 × 79   **d** 6 × 240

2 Look at the map of a 'Zoo bughouse'.

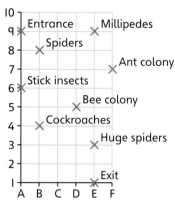

   a What will you find at

     i E1?

     ii D5?

     iii F7?

   b Where on the grid will you find

     i the spiders?

     ii the huge spiders?

     iii the entrance?

3a

3 Alan draws a shape on a grid.

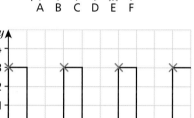

   a Write down the coordinates of the corners marked with a cross.

   b Write down two things you notice about these coordinates.

   c Will the coordinate (21, 3) have a cross?
Explain how you know.

4a

4 a Draw a pair of axes from 0 to 5.
Plot the graph for this table of values.

x	0	1	2	3	4
y	3	3	3	3	3

   b What is the the function for this graph?

 5b

5 Copy and complete this table of values for the rule $y = 3x - 2$.

x	1	2	3	4	
y					16

 5c

6 a Draw a pair of axes labelled from −10 to 10.
Plot these coordinate pairs and join them up with a straight line.

     (10, 6) (4, 0) (0, −4) (−5, −9) (−6, −10)

   b Copy this table. Use your graph to complete the table of values.

x	−4		3		9
y		−5		3	

 5a

17.4 Plotting real-life graphs

1 a Find the answer to these questions in the trapezium.
  i 10% of £120   **ii** 20% of £70
  ii 70% of £30   **iv** 90% of £20

  b Which number from the trapezium has not been used?

£18 £14
£12
£27 £21

2 'Carrie's Cabs' use this table to show customers the price of cab fares.

Distance (miles)	1	3	5	10
Cost (£)	2	6	10	20

  a Copy this grid. Plot the points in the table.
  b Join the points with a straight line.
  c Label your axes.
  d Give your graph a title.

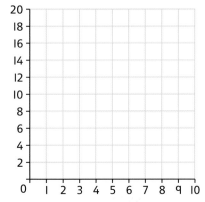

3 'Tom's Taxis' use this table to show customers the price of taxi fares.

Distance (miles)	1	3	5	10
Cost (£)	6	8	10	15

  a Copy this grid.
    Plot the points in the table.
  b Join the points with a straight line.
  c Label your axes and give your graph a title.
  d Use your graph to find out how much 'Tom's Taxis' charge to travel
    i 2 miles   **ii** 4 miles
    iii 8 miles   **iv** 9 miles.
  e Paul has £11.
    How far could he travel in 'Tom's Taxis'?

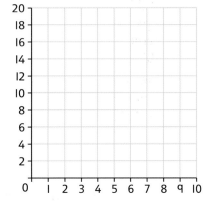

4 'Lomo's Limo's' charges £100 to hire a limo plus £2 per mile the limo is driven.
  a Copy and complete the table.

Distance (miles)	0	5	20	50
Cost (£)	100	110		

  b Copy this grid. Plot the points in the table.
  c Join the points with a straight line.
  d Label your axes and give your graph a title.
  e Use your graph to find out how much 'Lomo's Limo's' charge to travel
    i 15 miles   **ii** 40 miles
  f Evan's bill is £160.
    How far did he travel in 'Lomo's Limo's'?

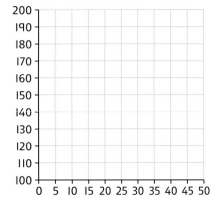

17.5 Using real-life graphs

1 Work out

a $\frac{3}{10} \times 40$ **b** $\frac{2}{3} \times 15$ **c** $\frac{2}{7} \times 21$ **d** $\frac{6}{11} \times 44$

2 Which sentence describes the graph?
  A As time goes on, I get closer to home
  B As time goes on, I get further from home
  C My distance from home does not change over time

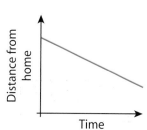

4a

4a

3 The graph shows the number of people per minute entering a zoo.

  a How many people per minute entered the zoo at 10:00?

  b At what time were 40 people per minute entering the zoo?

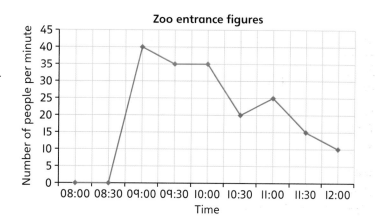

5a

4 This graph can be used to convert a length in centimeters to inches.
  Use the conversion graph to find these lengths in inches.

  a 10 cm

  b 4 cm

  c 32 cm

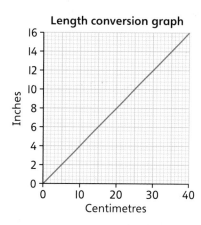

5a

5 Use the conversion graph from Q4 to convert these lengths in inches to centimetres.

  a 12 inches   **b** 2 inches   **c** 14 inches

17.6 Using formulae

1 Use partitioning to multiply these.

    a 13 × 5   **b** 26 × 4   **c** 28 × 6   **d** 62 × 4

Stan's café

Stan runs a cafe. His brother Peter runs a bistro. The name of the bistro is Pentos.

2 Peter sells cans of fizzy drinks for 15p more that he buys them, so

> selling price = buying price + 15p

Work out the selling prices for these buying prices.

    a lemonade 30p   **b** cola 32p   **c** orangeade 40p

3 The money that Peter takes from selling a lunch depends on price and how many are sold.
The price of lunch is £5, so

> money from sale of lunches = £5 × number sold

What is the total money taken from the sale of

    a 30 lunches?   **b** 35 lunches?   **c** 70 lunches?

4 Gill is the chef at Pentos. She is paid £12 an hour.
The total amount she earns depends on the number of hours worked as well as tips.

> amount Gill earns = £12 × number of hours + tips

How much does Gill earn if she works

    a 7 hours and gets a £5 tip?   **b** 8 hours and gets a £15 tip?

5 Gill uses three sausages in each 'Pentos breakfast'.
The total number of sausages can be found using the formula

> $x = 3y$

where x is the number of sausages and y is the number of breakfasts.
Work out the number of sausages for

    a 2 breakfasts   **b** 20 breakfasts   **c** 50 breakfasts.

6 Gill converts temperatures in degrees Celsius (°C) to degrees Fahrenheit (°F) using the approximate rule

> $F = 1.8C + 32$

    a Change these temperatures to degrees Fahrenheit.
      i 120°C   **ii** 155°C   **iii** 140°C
    b Change these temperatures to degrees Celsius.
      i 212°F   **ii** 230°F   **iii** 302°F

4a

4a

4a

5c

5b

17.7 More deriving formulae

1 This is a MCC (Mental Challenge Curve). Copy the curve.
Start at the first calculation, then in your head work out the missing values.

$7 \times 5 = \bigcirc \times 20 = \bigcirc \times 0.1 = \bigcirc \times 2.5 = \bigcirc - 75 = \bigcirc \div 20 = \bigcirc^2 = \bigcirc$

Peter's formulae
Peter's bistro is called 'Pentos' because all the tables seat 5 people.
Peter is going away on holiday with Stan and has left formula instructions
for his staff.

2 Many of the formulae for setting up each morning depend on the number
of tables n.
For each item, work out the number needed for six tables and for n tables.

a The number of flowers is six more than the number of tables.

b The number of candles is three more than the number of tables.

c The number of bread baskets is two less than the number of tables.

d Each table needs five chairs.

3 Some formulae depend on the number of customers x.
Peter has made up some formulae based on estimates.
For each item, find how many are needed for 50 customers and for x customers.

a The number of cappuccino cups is 20 less than the number of customers.

b The number of place mats is 10 more than the number of customers.

c The number of breadsticks is three times the number of customers.

d The number of tea cups is a half of the number of customers.

4 The 'Pentos Special' is a hot chocolate with five marshmallows on top and
two slices of slimmer's chocolate cake.

a Work out how many hot chocolates, marshmallows and slices of cake are
needed for 35 'Specials'

b Write a formula for each item for n 'Specials'.

5 The price of a hot chocolate with marshmallows is 95p.
Each slice of slimmer's chocolate cake costs 50p.

a What is the total price of a 'Pentos Special'?

b Write a formula for the price of a 'Pentos Special' if the price of a hot chocolate
with marshmallows is x pence and each slice of slimmer's chocolate cake
costs y pence.

c Write a formula for the change for the 'Pentos Special' from a £2 coin.

17.8 Using and checking equations

1 Copy and complete this multiplication square.

×	3			5
	12			
9	63			
			48	
7			56	
4				

2 Peter's bistro 'Pentos' has an outdoor section in the sun just for mathematicians!
The menu is written using algebra.

Pentos

all prices are in pence

Coffees	**Price**
Cappucino	$a + 20 = 119$
Latte	$b + 15 = 125$
Mocha	$c - 10 = 89$
Regular	$2d = 140$

Hot Chocolate

Luxury	$e + 12 = 162$
Mellow	$f \times 5 = 475$
Plain	$200 - g = 111$

Cakes

Slimmers' chocolate cake	$2h + 50 = 150$
Non-slimmers' chocolate cake	$3i - 50 = 175$
Carrot cake	$15 + 4j = 255$
Apple 'pi'	$3k + 55 = 400$

a Solve the equations on the menu to find the price of each item.

b Rewrite the menu for a non-mathematician.

3 Morgan asked for information about the Daily Special.
He was told

   "The total price of three vanilla slices and a 50p cup of tea is 155p"

Construct and solve an equation to find the price of a vanilla slice.

Play any game on the LiveText CD

18.1 Building shapes using triangles

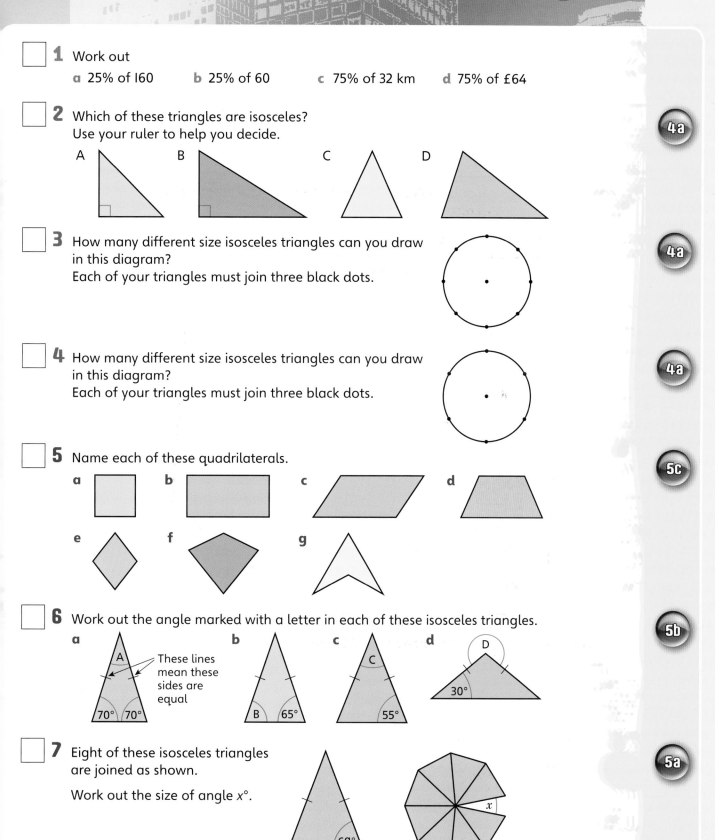

1 Work out

   a 25% of 160   **b** 25% of 60   **c** 75% of 32 km   **d** 75% of £64

2 Which of these triangles are isosceles?
Use your ruler to help you decide.

A   B   C   D

3 How many different size isosceles triangles can you draw in this diagram?
Each of your triangles must join three black dots.

4 How many different size isosceles triangles can you draw in this diagram?
Each of your triangles must join three black dots.

5 Name each of these quadrilaterals.

   a   **b**   **c**   **d**

   e   **f**   **g**

6 Work out the angle marked with a letter in each of these isosceles triangles.

   a   **b**   **c**   **d**

   A   These lines mean these sides are equal

   70° 70°   B 65°   C 55°   D 30°

7 Eight of these isosceles triangles are joined as shown.

   Work out the size of angle $x°$.

   69° x

18.2 Using ITC to understand reflection

1 Choose the number from the cloud which is the answer to these.

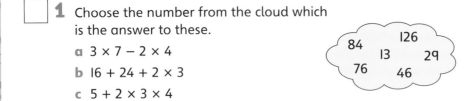

a $3 \times 7 - 2 \times 4$

b $16 + 24 + 2 \times 3$

c $5 + 2 \times 3 \times 4$

Cloud: 84   126   13   29   76   46

2 Sketch each shape and draw in any lines of symmetry.

A 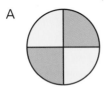 B C D

E F G

3 Copy these drawings and draw the image when the shape is reflected in the mirror (dotted) line

a 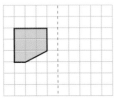 b 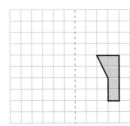 c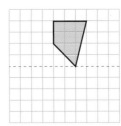

4 In Microsoft Word, use 'AutoShapes' to draw the following shapes.
Copy each shape.
Use 'Draw' then 'Rotate or Flip' to reflect the shape in the mirror line given

A B C D

3c

3b

4b

18.3 Understanding triangles and quadrilaterals

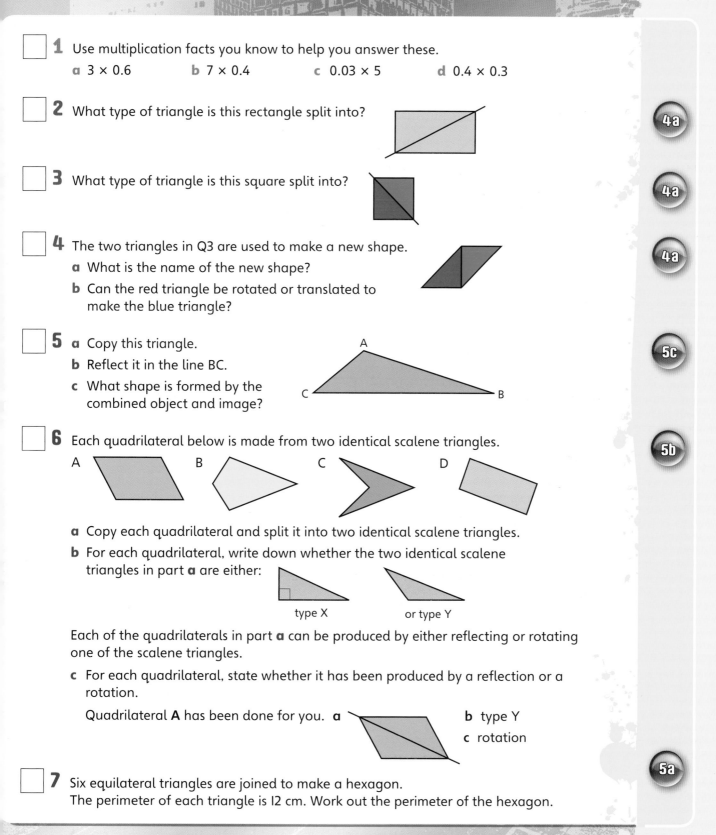

1 Use multiplication facts you know to help you answer these.

    a 3 × 0.6   **b** 7 × 0.4   **c** 0.03 × 5   **d** 0.4 × 0.3

2 What type of triangle is this rectangle split into?

3 What type of triangle is this square split into?

4 The two triangles in Q3 are used to make a new shape.

    a What is the name of the new shape?

    b Can the red triangle be rotated or translated to make the blue triangle?

5 **a** Copy this triangle.

    b Reflect it in the line BC.

    c What shape is formed by the combined object and image?

6 Each quadrilateral below is made from two identical scalene triangles.

    a Copy each quadrilateral and split it into two identical scalene triangles.

    b For each quadrilateral, write down whether the two identical scalene triangles in part **a** are either:

        type X   or type Y

Each of the quadrilaterals in part **a** can be produced by either reflecting or rotating one of the scalene triangles.

    c For each quadrilateral, state whether it has been produced by a reflection or a rotation.

    Quadrilateral **A** has been done for you. **a**

        b type Y

        c rotation

7 Six equilateral triangles are joined to make a hexagon.
The perimeter of each triangle is 12 cm. Work out the perimeter of the hexagon.

18.4 Cubes and other 3-D shapes

1 Find the remainder when 373 is divided by 7.

2 **a** How many faces does a cube have?

b How many edges does a cube have?

c How many vertices does a cube have?

3 Which of these shapes are prisms?

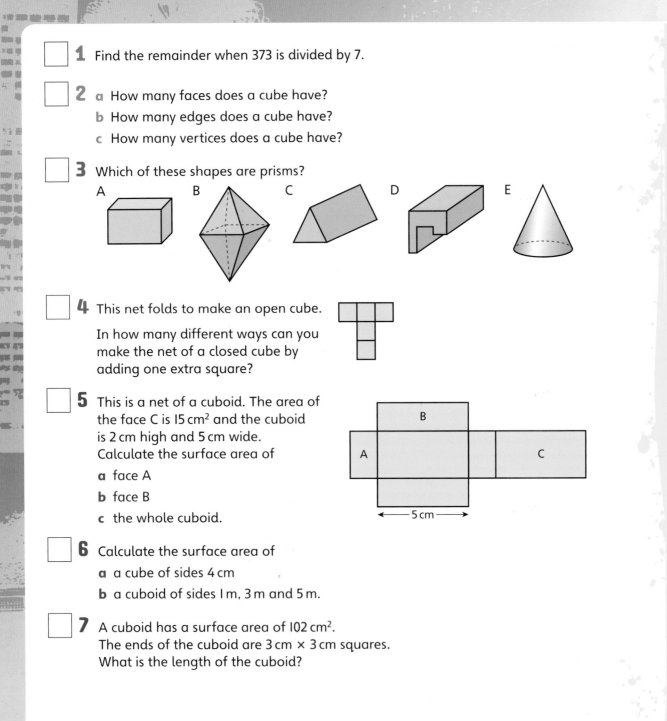

4 This net folds to make an open cube.

In how many different ways can you make the net of a closed cube by adding one extra square?

5 This is a net of a cuboid. The area of the face C is 15 cm² and the cuboid is 2 cm high and 5 cm wide. Calculate the surface area of

a face A

b face B

c the whole cuboid.

6 Calculate the surface area of

a a cube of sides 4 cm

b a cuboid of sides 1 m, 3 m and 5 m.

7 A cuboid has a surface area of 102 cm².
The ends of the cuboid are 3 cm × 3 cm squares.
What is the length of the cuboid?

3a

4b

4b

5b

5b

5b

18.5 Constructing 3-D shapes

1 Without using a calculator, copy and complete this addition pyramid. The number in each brick is found by adding the two bricks below it.

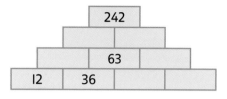

2 Draw the accurate net of a cube of side length 3 cm.

3 Draw an accurate net for this cuboid.

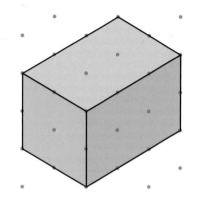

4 Draw an accurate net for this triangular prism.

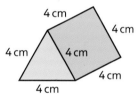

5 Draw an accurate net for this triangular prism.

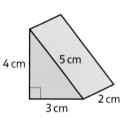

6 Draw an accurate net for this square based pyramid.

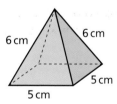

7 Look again at Q2 to 6 and add flaps to the nets so that you could make each 3-D shape.

Look at this sketch for the net of a regular tetrahedron. Construct a net for this tetrahedron with side length 4 cm.

18.6 Angles, triangles and pyramids

1 Write a number sentence that gives the target answer. You must use each of the numbers 1, 2, 3 and 5 only once. You can use any of these: +, −, ×, ÷ and brackets as many times as you want.

The first one is done for you.

  a Target = 17   Answer: (3 + 5) × 2 + 1 = 17

  b Target = 11   **c** Target = 6   **d** Target = 30   **e** Target = 45

2 Look at this diagram.

Measure angle A.

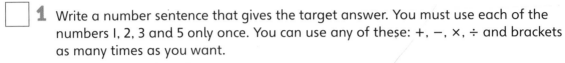

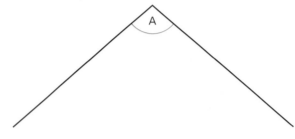

3 **a** Draw a horizontal line the same length as BD.

  b Draw a line 20° above BD from B in the direction of C.

  c Draw a line 12° below BD from B in the direction of E.

4 **a** Make an accurate copy of this diagram.

  b Measure the distance in a straight line from A to B.

5 Make accurate copies of these triangles.

  a   **b**

6 Make an accurate copy of this face of a pyramid with a base length of 8 cm.

NOTES